The Pingry School Library

Gift of

Dedication Fund

1966

S I D N E Y   G O L D E N

Department of Chemistry · Brandeis University

ELEMENTS

OF THE

THEORY OF GASES

ADDISON-WESLEY PUBLISHING COMPANY, INC.

READING, MASSACHUSETTS · PALO ALTO · LONDON

This book is in the

ADDISON-WESLEY SERIES IN CHEMISTRY

Francis T. Bonner, *Consulting Editor*

PREFACE

The kinetic theory of gases is an outstanding example of a physical theory which is closely tied to the experimental phenomena it seeks to elaborate. As a result, it can serve as a splendid vehicle to implant firmly in the minds of students the intimate relationship that prevails between physical theory and experimental results. The presentation given in this book has attempted to emphasize such a relationship.

Beginning with a few intuitively clear assumptions as to the physical nature of gases, we quickly come to an elaborate and sophisticated mathematical theory of gases. For the student to appreciate the scope of the theory, some of the mathematical flavor inherent in the theory must be communicated. I have attempted to do this without at the same time making excessive demands of mathematical prowess on the part of the student. The preparation of a good course in calculus should be adequate, since the mathematical arguments used are presented in explicit terms and need simply to be followed. Nevertheless, the emphasis here is placed upon the use to which the experimental facts can be put in developing the theory which purports to account for them. The first two chapters are thus concerned exclusively with an exposition of certain selected experimental results. To facilitate the subsequent mathematical encounters by the student, however, the selected properties of both uniform and nonuniform gases are appropriately dealt with in the quantitative language of mathematics. The impact of the experimental facts upon the formulation of the theory can be made most effective in this way. With the help of mathematics, intuition can be forged into a powerful scientific tool. I hope that the treatment presented here illustrates how.

The remaining three chapters relate primarily to the construction of a simple kinetic theory of gases. Simplicity is a subjective term, but should not be confused with an abandonment of sound reasoning, which I have attempted to retain. For this purpose, and to avoid undue complexity, some of the theory has been cast into a form which renders it incomplete, although formally correct. Perhaps such a mode of presentation will appeal to the student wishing to know the shortcomings of the simple theory; hopefully, it may show him questions still unanswered and problems still unsolved at an elementary level. An accompanying feature of a good theory, and such is the case in point, is the grist it furnishes to the experimental mill. The theoretical pace of the last three chapters has not neglected this aspect. The inference of the Maxwell-Boltzmann distribution is ultimately justified only by the results of experiments not previously incorporated into the theory.

Before, during, and after the writing of this book, I have been fortunate to receive much help from many sources, for which I am deeply grateful. The students who have worked through a preliminary version have left their mark upon the pages which follow. The rendition of what was merely a collection of notes into the final typescript of this book was beautifully carried out by Mrs. Barbara MacDonald. The result has been read—and assented to or dissented from, in varying degrees—by several people to whom I am indebted for their comments and suggestions: I. Amdur, S. Berko, F. T. Bonner, D. R. Herschbach, and K. S. Kustin. As a result of the suggestions which were made, fewer ambiguities and errors are to be found in the following pages than would otherwise be the case.

The editorial and art departments of the publisher have given a form to the book it otherwise would not have had, and I am indeed thankful for their efforts. Finally, I gratefully acknowledge the varied help my daughters, Harriet and Nancy, have given in bringing this book to completion.

Lexington, Mass.   S. G.
January, 1964

CONTENTS

1. PROPERTIES OF UNIFORM GASES

1. Uniform state variables of a gas 1
2. Equation of state of uniform gases—low pressures 11
3. The ideal gas 16
4. Gases at high pressures 20
5. Equations of state of uniform gases—high pressures 24
6. Critical phenomena and corresponding states 34
7. Summary 37

2. PROPERTIES OF NONUNIFORM GASES

1. Behavior of nonuniform gases 40
2. Thermal conductivity in gases 43
3. Mass transport in gases 49
4. Viscous behavior of gases 53
5. Correlations among transport properties 56
6. Summary 58

3. KINETIC-MOLECULAR THEORY OF IDEAL GASES

1. Molecular features of an ideal gas 60
2. Mechanics of particles 63
3. Equation of state of uniform ideal gases 78
4. Effusion 84
5. Summary 88

4. MOLECULAR DISTRIBUTIONS

1. Probability and averages 92
2. Maxwell's velocity distribution 101
3. The Maxwell-Boltzmann distribution 113
4. Multiple molecular distributions in ideal gases 116
5. Summary 119

5. NONIDEAL GASES

1. Modifications of ideal gas theory 122
2. Application to intramolecular motion 124
3. Molecular collisions 130
4. Simple theory of transport properties 136
5. The covolume equation of state 145
6. Summary 149

REFERENCES 151

INDEX 152

To my daughters

1 · PROPERTIES OF UNIFORM GASES

1. UNIFORM STATE VARIABLES OF A GAS

Of the many measurable properties which a gas may be said to have, e.g., its color, solubility in water, chemical reactivity towards oxygen, a few relate most simply and directly to the gaseous state. For a specified gas, these are the *mass* of the gas, its *temperature*, the *volume* of the container in which it is confined, and the *pressure* which it exerts upon the walls of the container. To be added to these properties is the *kind* of gas. When a mixture of several gases is involved, the *chemical composition* is a measurable property which serves to give a chemical characterization of the gaseous mixture. When the gas consists of a single chemically pure substance, its chemical composition is denoted when the kind of gas is stipulated. Just how these properties are related for gases will be discussed later.

The properties of a gas often may yield measured values which are related to the region of the gas in which the measurements are carried out. Thus we can imagine, as illustrated in Fig. 1–1, a chemically pure gas confined in a container consisting of an interconnected network of regions. In each region, the mass, volume, pressure, and temperature of the gas contained there may have values different from those in other regions. When such is the case, we are dealing with a *nonuniform* gas. However, we may imagine any nonuniform gas as corresponding, in a limiting sense, to a

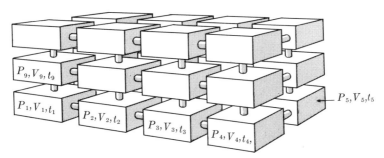

Fig. 1–1. Schematic model of nonuniform gas. Each small region is uniform and different from other regions.

number of connected regions of arbitrarily small size and extent, each of which is uniform. For this reason, particular stress may be placed initially upon the properties of *uniform* gases.

Two classes of properties arise, which we now consider. The first of these consists of *extensive* properties and is illustrated by the volume of a gas. The second class of properties consists of *intensive* properties and is illustrated by the pressure exerted by a gas. Stated loosely, the former exhibit measured values which, under conditions to be made explicit presently, are proportional to the extent of the gas; the latter give measured values which, for uniform gases, are independent of the extent of the gas. If a uniform gas is divided into two parts, as by introducing a negligibly thin partition into the container confining it, the pressures in each part will be identical and will have the same value as measured originally before the partition was introduced. The same will be true for the temperatures and compositions. On the other hand, the volumes and masses of each part may be different. The volume of each part will be directly proportional to its corresponding mass under the stated conditions. The property of *density*, which is defined as the ratio of mass to the corresponding volume, is seen to be independent of the extent of the system and is an intensive property. In the illustration considered, the densities in each part will be the same and equal to the value obtained prior to partition of the original gas.

It is evident that intensive properties may have nonzero measured values for any region, however small. We can thus adopt a criterion for the uniformity of a gas: it is uniform if and only if each of its intensive properties has the same value regardless of the region of the gas in which it is measured. In these terms, the extensive properties of a uniform gas are then proportional to its mass.

Each of the properties which has been mentioned is capable of exhibiting a wide range of measured values. To illustrate: gases have been observed at pressures ranging from practically zero values to many thousand times the pressure exerted by the earth's atmosphere at sea level, and at temperatures ranging from $-272°C$ to well over $5000°C$. Even these ranges may be exceeded, but they serve to illustrate the extent of variability possible. However, whether the range of values of a measured property is large or small is not entirely relevant to our purpose. The point here is illustrated by the existence of nitrogen-oxygen gas mixtures at ordinary temperatures and pressures which range in composition from just under 100% oxygen to just under 100% nitrogen. What is important is that there be, in fact, some nonzero range of values. In this circumstance, we must be prepared to give a description of gases which may exist under a variety of *conditions*, e.g., low temperature and low pressure, as well as high temperature and high pressure, and other combinations, in the illustrations noted previously.

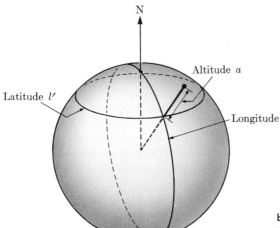

N

Altitude a

Latitude l'

Longitude

Fig. 1–2. Location of object by latitude, longitude, and altitude.

Each condition of a gas which is completely distinguishable from any other condition will be referred to as a *state* of the gas. For a (uniform) gas consisting of a chemically pure substance, e.g., hydrogen, neon, water vapor, each set of measured values (for the same gas) of mass m, volume V, pressure P, and temperature t corresponds experimentally to a single distinct condition of the relevant gas and, therefore, to one of its states. For such a situation, the set of measured values (m, V, P, t) is to be regarded as synonymous with the word "state." When dealing with mixtures, the previous list of measurable properties must be augmented by the inclusion of the composition of the gases. If this property is simply denoted by c, the set of measured values (c, m, V, P, t) is to be identified with the state of a gas. In mathematical terms, two states of a gas, $(c_1, m_1, V_1, P_1, t_1)$ and $(c_2, m_2, V_2, P_2, t_2)$, are defined as identical if and only if the corresponding measured values of identical properties are equal, i.e., $c_1 = c_2$, $m_1 = m_2$, etc.

The situation which has been described is entirely similar to others in physics and chemistry, where the notion of state is introduced in order to refer to a completely characterized condition. As illustrated in Fig. 1–2, the location of an object in the atmosphere of the earth is determinable from a specification of its altitude a measured from the surface of the earth, its longitude l, and its latitude l'. Whatever we may wish to use these quantities for, it is apparent that the location of two objects will be the same if and only if the corresponding altitudes, longitudes, and latitudes of the two objects are identical. In this illustration, the "location state" of an object consists of a set of three numbers, (a, l, l'). The notion that an appropriate list of measurable properties is *sufficient* to characterize the relevant state of a system is tacitly assumed here, but it is supported by experimental evidence.

The measurable properties we have enumerated are each conveniently referred to as a *state variable* of the gaseous system. The state of a system thus may be thought of as a *function* of its state variables. Any alteration of the latter is necessarily associated with a change in the former, in spite of the absence of an explicit mathematical function or formula relating the state to its pertinent state variables.

As we have repeatedly mentioned, the state variables of a uniform gas are measurable quantities. Each measured value of such a property is one of its possible values. If a quantitative description of gaseous properties is to be given, it is important to know how to determine each value precisely. This sort of knowledge is appropriately dealt with in the laboratory, but a brief recapitulation here seems desirable.

The measurement of the volume of a gas requires simply a measurement of the volume of the container confining it. This is possible because gases seem characteristically to fill any container, whatever its volume. Such behavior seemingly distinguishes gases from liquids and solids. (However, the distinction to be made between gases and liquids is somewhat subtle, as we shall see later.) Because containers can be manufactured in various sizes of prescribed or known volume, the measurement of the volume of a gas is almost trivial. It is important, however, to be able to alter the volume of a given sample of gas in certain experiments. This is accomplished by altering the volume of its container in a known way. A simple device, a *gas burette*, illustrated in schematic terms in Fig. 1–3, accomplishes this. As the piston is moved from one mark to another, the volume of the confined gas is altered from one value to another, as determined by the construction of the device.

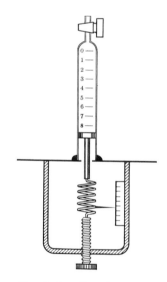

Fig. 1–3.   Gas burette with spring piston.

When the measured volume of a gas is specified, the resulting quantity is a combination of two things: (1) a number, and (2) a physical unit. To illustrate, we might have a volume of 10.0 cm^3. The same volume (to a comparable degree of accuracy) can be expressed as 0.61 in^3. Other combinations are also possible, where the same volume, to an accuracy of 1%, can be expressed in numbers and units that are quite different. It is thus important to keep track of the units, if the numbers are to mean anything at all. (We shall return to the matter of units shortly.)

The measurement of the mass of a sample of gas is easily carried out in principle. In practice, because of the relatively small mass of a gas compared with the mass of its container, such measurements can be carried out precisely only with some difficulty, since it is necessary that precise measurements be made of the mass of the container alone, and also of the container and the gas. The mass of the latter may then be found as the difference between two large quantities.

Usually, in determining the mass of an object, a *balance* is used to weigh it. The gravitational force exerted upon the object—its weight—is balanced against the gravitational force exerted upon a mass of known value. The two weights are said to be identical under such conditions. However, in an actual weighing, the forces involved also include those due to *buoyancy* of the objects in the "sea of air" surrounding them. These must be compensated for either by experimental means or by calculations, in order to have a correct measure of the gravitational forces. The force ascribable to the buoyancy of an object is the weight of a volume of air equivalent to the volume of the object—the so-called *displaced* volume of air. The buoyancy correction thus is comparable to the weight of gases to be measured.

For our purposes, we may assume that a measurement of the mass of a gas, when needed, is capable of being made with an accuracy that is adequate. We shall usually employ mass units of *grams*. This unit will be designated by gm (i.e., *grams-mass*). Occasionally, we will use *grams* for units of *force*, corresponding to the *weight* of an object. This unit will be designated by gf (i.e., *grams-force*).

The pressure exerted by a uniform gas, as already mentioned, is an intensive property, and so it may be measured in any region of the gas with the assurance that the same value will be obtained. In particular, it may be measured conveniently at an interior surface of the vessel containing the gas. For example, the gas burette can be designed so that the force required to maintain the piston stationary is measured. We may suppose that the forces exhibited by various springs have been determined independently, and the latter are employed to maintain the stationary piston. With an appropriate design, forces due to friction of the piston may be kept to a negligible value. Therefore the force applied to the piston by an appropriate spring must be equal in magnitude (but opposite in direction) to that produced by the gas. From the definition

$$\text{Pressure} = \frac{\text{force}}{\text{area}}, \tag{1–1}$$

a knowledge of the area of the piston allows us to compute the pressure of the gas acting upon it.

A variation of the arrangement which has been described, involving no difference in principle, makes use of the *hydrostatic pressure* of a liquid to measure the pressure exerted by a uniform gas. As indicated in Fig. 1–4, the piston of the gas burette is replaced by a liquid, which serves the same purpose of confining the gas in the vessel. The pressure exerted upon the stationary surface of the liquid by the gas is equal to the hydrostatic pressure of the liquid immediately below the liquid surface. The latter, in turn, must be equal to the hydrostatic pressure of the liquid at any point of the liquid having the same vertical distance from a plane parallel to the earth's surface. With an appropriate design, as indicated in the illustration, the pressure at such a point can be calculated in terms of the height of the column of liquid which is supported above this point. We shall presently indicate how this is done, but we turn first to the units in which pressure is expressed.

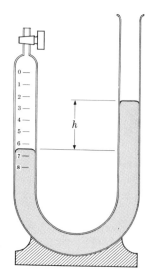

Fig. 1–4. Gas burette with manometer.

From the relation given in Eq. (1–1), the units employed for pressure are determined by those used for force and area. Common units for force are the *dyne* and the *pound* (the latter corresponding to the force of the earth's gravitational attraction of one "pound" of matter at sea level). From these are derived the pressure units: dynes/cm^2 and lb/in^2. Since a given pressure has a value depending upon the units in terms of which it is expressed, the relations existing between various units is worth examining. In familiar terms, the gravitational force exerted at sea level by the earth upon a mass of one gram varies with latitude. However, a standard value is 980.665 dynes. This can be expressed mathematically as ($\backsimeq$ is to be read as "is equivalent to")

$$1 \text{ gram-force} \backsimeq 980.665 \text{ dynes,}$$

or

$$1 \backsimeq 980.665 \text{ dynes/gram-force.}$$

In a similar manner we may write, with abbreviations,

$$1 \backsimeq 453.592 \text{ gf/lb,}$$

and

$$1 \backsimeq 6.45163 \text{ cm}^2/\text{in}^2.$$

If we treat each of the quantities in parentheses as an algebraic quantity in an algebraic equation, we obtain the following expression:

$$1 \approx \frac{980.665 \text{ (dynes/gf)} \times 453.592 \text{ (gf/lb)}}{6.45163 \text{ cm}^2/\text{in}^2}$$

$$= \frac{980.665 \times 453.592}{6.45163} \frac{\text{dynes/cm}^2}{\text{lb/in}^2}$$

$$= 6.8947 \times 10^4 \frac{\text{dynes·cm}^{-2}}{\text{lb·in}^{-2}}.$$

This quantity represents a *conversion factor* relating the two units of pressure which have been mentioned.

A convenient unit of pressure is a value ascribed to the atmosphere at sea level. Since both the sea level and the pressure actually observed may vary considerably, this unit must be understood as a *defined* quantity (as, in fact, are all the others we have mentioned). It is defined by the relation

$$1 \approx 14.696 \text{ lb·in}^{-2}/\text{atmosphere.}$$

This relation may be combined with the previous one to give

$$1 \approx 1.01325 \times 10^6 \text{ dynes·cm}^{-2}/\text{atm,}$$

an enormous number, compared with the previous one.

A pressure unit used more frequently relates to the hydrostatic means of its measurement, which is illustrated in Fig. 1–4. Any two points in the liquid having the same vertical height (as measured from the surface of the earth) must have the same pressure. Hence the pressure at the surface of the liquid confining the gas must be equal to the pressure at an equivalent point indicated in the diagram. The latter, however, has an additional column of liquid to support. If the cross section of the tube at this level is A (cm^2) and the additional height is h (cm), the volume of liquid being supported above this level is Ah (cm^3). If the density of liquid is ρ (gm/cm^2), the mass of liquid supported is ρAh (gm). The resulting pressure is the force (or weight) per unit area and is simply ρh (gf/cm^2), eliminating the area. This pressure contribution must be the difference in pressure between two points differing in distance by h (cm). Of course, the units are not those which we have used previously, so we must relate them. If we take the pressure difference to be ΔP, we must have

$$\Delta P = \rho h \text{ (gf/cm}^2), \qquad (1\text{--}2)$$

then

$$\Delta P = \frac{\rho h \text{ (gf·cm}^{-2}) \times 980.665 \text{ (dynes·gf}^{-1})}{1.01325 \times 10^6 \text{ dynes·cm}^{-2}/\text{atm}},$$

$$= 0.967 \times 10^{-3} \rho h \text{ atm.}$$

TABLE 1–1

PRESSURE CONVERSION FACTORS*

	atmosphere	dyne·cm^{-2}	mm Hg	bar	lb·in^{-2}	kgf·cm^{-2}
atmosphere	1	1.01325×10^6	760	1.0133	14.696	1.0332
dyne·cm^{-2}	9.8692×10^{-7}	1	7.5006×10^{-4}	1.000×10^{-6}	1.4504×10^{-5}	1.0197×10^{-6}
mm Hg	1.3158×10^{-3}	1.3332×10^3	1	1.3332×10^{-3}	1.9337×10^2	1.3595×10^{-3}
bar	0.98692	1.000×10^6	750.06	1	14.504	1.0197
lb·in^{-2}	6.8046×10^{-2}	6.8947×10^4	51.715	6.8947×10^{-2}	1	7.0307×10^{-2}
kgf·cm^{-2}	0.96784	9.8067×10^5	73.556	0.98067	14.223	1

* Table is to be used as follows: a unit in the left column is equivalent to each of the quantities in the same row.

One of the liquids commonly employed as a *manometric* fluid is mercury. At a temperature of 0°C, it has a density of 13.5951 gm/cm^3. Hence for mercury,

$$\Delta P = \frac{h}{76.00} \text{ atm.}$$

In previous terms, we have

$$1 \approx 76.00 \text{ cm Hg/atm.}$$

The various conversion factors for pressure are summarized in Table 1–1.

Any recapitulation of the measurable properties of uniform gases must include the measurement of their temperature. In such measurements a *thermometer* is employed. When the reading indicated by the thermometer is unchanging, for however long it is in thermal contact with the gas, we say that the temperature of the gas is that indicated by the reading on the thermometer. We need not inquire into the precise details of the thermometer except to note that it has been prepared with reliable markings of a universal scale of temperature. A common scale of temperature is the *celsius* scale (invented in 1742 by Anders Celsius, and familiarly known as the *centigrade* scale): the numerical value of temperature is taken as 0°C at the normal freezing point of pure water and 100°C at the normal boiling point of pure water. There are thus one hundred degrees (of temperature) between the freezing and boiling points of pure water on the celsius scale. Another common scale is the *fahrenheit* scale. Here, the normal freezing point of pure water has the value of 32°F. There are one hundred and eighty degrees (of temperature) between the freezing and boiling points of pure water on the fahrenheit scale. That is,

$$1 \approx \frac{180 \text{ degrees fahrenheit}}{100 \text{ degrees celsius}} = 1.80 \, \frac{°F}{°C} \, .$$

The two *temperature scales* are *linearly* related through the following equation:

$$\text{temp (°F)} = 32°F + 1.8 \frac{°F}{°C} \times \text{temp (°C)}. \tag{1-3}$$

In the course of experiments requiring the maintenance of a fixed, known temperature, a device known as a *thermostat* is often employed. Such a device usually involves a large uniform mass of substance at a fixed temperature (which may be adjusted to suit the experiment). It is inherent that the temperature of the thermostat be alterable only to a very small extent by contact with a gaseous system. In principle, and this is well-approximated by actual design, the temperature change of the thermostat is negligible during the course of any experiment. Systems placed in thermal contact with a thermostat ultimately will assume the temperature of the thermostat. In a sense, therefore, the thermostat is a massive thermometer whose temperature is easily measured by some other thermometer.

Another kind of thermostat takes advantage of the fact that certain heterogeneous mixtures of pure substances can exist as such only at fixed temperatures. For example, a mixture of pure liquid and solid water at atmospheric pressure can coexist in equilibrium only at 0°C. (This situation defines the temperature, in fact.) Regardless of the amount of liquid or solid, the temperature is the same.

Finally, the chemical composition of a gas is a measurable property. Ultimately, the individual molecular constituents of the gas must be separated from one another and identified. Depending upon the actual nature of the constituents of the gas, either physical or chemical means may be employed to accomplish this result. How this is done in each individual case cannot be elaborated in detail. For a general discussion, far too much chemistry is entailed. In simple cases, liquefaction of the gas, followed by a careful distillation of the liquid, will result in a good separation of the gas into its individual molecular constituents. In certain special cases, chemical reactions can remove certain of the constituents from the gas. Thus, a mixture of carbon dioxide and nitrogen can be bubbled through a concentrated aqueous solution of sodium hydroxide, to absorb the former by converting it to soluble sodium carbonate.

The chemical composition of a gas may be expressed in a variety of ways. The simplest one is in terms of the *weight* (or mass) *fraction* of each constituent. A more useful expression, as we shall see, is in terms of the *mole fraction* of each constituent. The relation between these two types of compositional variables is a direct one involving the molecular weights of the constituent gases. Let us consider a gas of three constituents, A, B, C, of molecular weights W_A, W_B, and W_C, respectively. The respective weight fractions are f_A, f_B, and f_C, and we seek the corresponding mole fractions x_A, x_B, and x_C. We have

$$f_A = \frac{m_A}{m_A + m_B + m_C}, \qquad f_B = \frac{m_B}{m_A + m_B + m_C},$$

$$f_C = \frac{m_C}{m_A + m_B + m_C},$$

where m_A, m_B, and m_C are the masses (or weights) of the respective gas constituents. The masses may be expressed in *grams*, and the molecular weights are then expressed in *grams/gram-mole*. Clearly,

$$\frac{f_B}{f_A} = \frac{m_B}{m_A} \quad \text{and} \quad \frac{f_C}{f_A} = \frac{m_C}{m_A}.$$

Now, the mole ratios are given by

$$\frac{n_B}{n_A} = \frac{m_B/W_B}{m_A/W_A} = \frac{f_B/W_B}{f_A/W_A} \quad \text{and} \quad \frac{n_C}{n_A} = \frac{m_C/W_C}{m_A/W_A} = \frac{f_C/W_C}{f_A/W_A}.$$

Hence,

$$x_A = \frac{n_A}{n_A + n_B + n_C} = \frac{1}{1 + \dfrac{n_B}{n_A} + \dfrac{n_C}{n_A}}$$

$$= \frac{1}{1 + \dfrac{f_B/W_B}{f_A/W_A} + \dfrac{f_C/W_C}{f_A/W_A}} = \frac{f_A/W_A}{f_A/W_A + f_B/W_B + f_C/W_C}.$$

Similar expressions are obtained for x_B and x_C. Regardless of the *kind* of fraction employed to characterize the chemical composition of a gas, it is *dimensionless*, although the kind must be specified for the sake of clarity. In these terms the composition variables are intensive properties of a uniform gas.

Throughout this book, we shall have occasion to employ mathematical equations which involve physical quantities, i.e., the measurable properties of gases. Since the values of the latter quantities are associated with numerical quantities and units, the equations must be consistent with respect to both of these. Quantities which may appear in the equations as symbols must be understood to have some sort of units, of such a kind as to satisfy the equation *dimensionally* as well as numerically.

2. EQUATION OF STATE OF UNIFORM GASES—LOW PRESSURES

Having fixed in mind the various measurable properties of a gas, we now take note of an extremely important experimental fact. The variables, pressure, temperature, volume, mass, and composition of a uniform gas, have values which are related to one another. Stated differently, restricting certain of the variables to specified values implies that the remaining ones must have fixed values, and so long as the former are fixed, the latter are incapable of alteration. (Just how many and which of the variables must be specified to fix, or determine, the values of the others will be elaborated subsequently.) It is our object to give a quantitative expression to this experimental fact.

We begin with the simplest kind of gas, a chemically pure gas consisting of a single molecular constituent. As examples, we may think of pure hydrogen, nitrogen, carbon dioxide, etc. For such a uniform gas there is no need to consider the composition. Its intensive variables may be restricted to pressure and temperature, while its extensive variables are restricted to mass and volume. The experimental facts are compactly summarized in the mathematical statement

$$F(m, V, P, t) = 0, \tag{1–4}$$

which asserts that there is a mathematical function F relating the values of the mass, volume, pressure, and temperature of a pure uniform gas. This may be expressed equivalently as:

$P = P(m, V, t)$,　or pressure is a function of mass, volume, and temperature;

$V = V(m, P, t)$,　or volume is a function of mass, pressure, and temperature;

$t = t(m, V, P)$,　or temperature is a function of mass, volume, and pressure.

In particular, the second of these is useful. Because of the extensive nature of V and m, we must have

$$V = mV(1, P, t).$$

Since the function indicated has only P and t as variables and refers to a unit of mass, we may rewrite the equation as

$$V = mv(P, t), \tag{1–5}$$

where v is the volume function for a unit of mass, and is termed the *specific volume* of the gas. Equation (1–5), apart from the functional dependence

TABLE 1–2

SPECIFIC VOLUMES (LITERS/GRAM) FOR CERTAIN GASES
AT VARIOUS TEMPERATURES AND PRESSURES*

Hydrogen

	1 atm	100 atm	200 atm	300 atm
0°C	11.13	1.189×10^{-1}	0.6375×10^{-1}	0.448×10^{-1}
50°C	13.16	1.391×10^{-1}	0.735×10^{-1}	0.517×10^{-1}
100°C	15.19	1.595×10^{-1}	0.843×10^{-1}	0.588×10^{-1}

Carbon monoxide

	1 atm	50 atm	100 atm	200 atm
0°C	0.800	1.566×10^{-2}	0.795×10^{-2}	0.408×10^{-2}
50°C	0.946	1.890×10^{-2}	0.956×10^{-2}	0.525×10^{-2}
100°C	1.093	2.211×10^{-2}	1.125×10^{-2}	0.592×10^{-2}

Oxygen

	1 atm	100 atm	200 atm	400 atm
0°C	0.723	0.653×10^{-2}	0.322×10^{-2}	0.185×10^{-2}
100°C	—	0.969×10^{-2}	0.506×10^{-2}	0.270×10^{-2}
200°C	—	—	0.640×10^{-2}	0.346×10^{-2}

* Computed from data given in J. R. Partington, *Advanced Treatise on Physical Chemistry*, Vol. I, pp. 571, 577. London: Longmans, Green and Company (1949).

which has been indicated, is simply related to the definition of density, the latter being the reciprocal of the specific volume.

For a pure gas, we need deal only with the specific volume function. In Table 1–2 are data for several pure gases which relate to the point under discussion. It can be seen that for a fixed value of the temperature the specific volume of a gas generally decreases markedly as its pressure increases. For a fixed value of the pressure, the specific volume increases slightly with increasing temperature. We shall be interested in the precise mathematical function $v(P, t)$ which represents the data accurately. However, studies made of such data over the past three hundred years have revealed no simple mathematical expression which can account for all of the data. To emphasize this complexity, certain of the data of Table 1–2 have been plotted in Fig. 1–5. Explicitly, we have plotted the values of $Pv(P, t)$ versus P for fixed values of t. [Since $v(P, t)$ is a function of pressure and

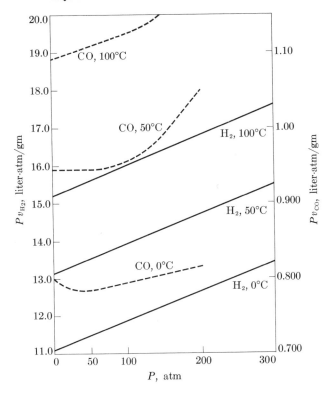

Fig. 1–5. *Pv* vs. *P* for hydrogen and carbon monoxide. (Data of Table 1–2.)

temperature, so is $Pv(P, t)$. The choice we have made is suggested by *Boyle's Law*, which we consider below.] The remarkable feature of these graphs is the behavior to be observed at low values of the pressure: as the pressure of a gas at fixed temperature is made smaller and smaller, the product of the specific volume and the pressure approaches a finite nonzero value. Stated differently, under the foregoing conditions the limiting specific volume varies inversely with the pressure. This is the celebrated behavior of gases discovered by Sir Robert Boyle in 1661. We may state it mathematically as

$$Pv = C \text{ (independent of } P, v \text{) as } P \to 0. \qquad (1\text{–}6)$$

Notice again should be taken of the fact that equations employing physical quantities, like Eq. (1–6), involve both numerical quantities and units. As discussed earlier, equations involving physical quantities must be dimensionally consistent. In Eq. (1–6), the choice of *atmosphere* for the unit of pressure and *liter/gm* for the unit of specific volume means that the constant C must be expressed in units of *liter·atm/gm*.

TABLE 1–3

$C(t)$ FOR HYDROGEN AND CARBON MONOXIDE

	0°C	50°C	100°C
Hydrogen	11.13	13.16	15.19
Carbon monoxide	.800	0.946	1.093
Ratio $C_{H_2}(t)/C_{CO}(t)$	13.91	13.92	13.89
W_{CO}/W_{H_2}	13.91	13.91	13.91

Now, the constant C is not simply a universal number. It is constant only with respect to changes in pressure and specific volume. Upon what may it then depend? Since each graph of Fig. 1–5 is related to a fixed gas and temperature, we can anticipate that C may change if either of these, or both, is changed. That such is the case is indicated in Table 1–3. We examine, first, the variation of C from gas to gas at the same temperature. The fact emerges that the ratio of two C's (at the same temperature) is equal to the reciprocal of the ratios of their molecular weights. That is,

$$\frac{C_A(t)}{C_B(t)} = \frac{W_B}{W_A},$$

or

$$W_A C_A(t) = W_B C_B(t), \tag{1–7}$$

and this relation is *independent of temperature*. Equation (1–7) is a statement which can be rationalized with a molecular theory of the constitution of gases through *Avogadro's hypothesis:* equal volumes of gases at the same temperature and pressure contain equal numbers of molecules. Therefore, for gases which have the same number of molecules, Eq. (1–6) can be written in a universal form for *all* pure gases,

$$P\overline{V} = WC(t) = K(t), \tag{1–8}$$

where $\overline{V}(=Wv)$ is the volume per gram-mole of the gas (i.e., molal volume) and $K(t)$ is a quantity, the same for all pure gases, which depends only upon the temperature of the gas.

We examine next the temperature dependence of K. This is done with the help of the data of Table 1–3. In Fig. 1–6, several K's have been calculated and plotted as a function of temperature. The linear relationship which is obtained embodies *Charles's Law* and can be expressed mathematically as

$$K(t) = (t°C + 273.16)R, \tag{1–9}$$

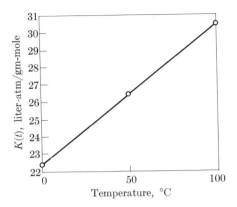

Fig. 1–6. Variation of K(t) with temperature.

where R is, now, a constant universally applicable to all pure gases. If we define a temperature scale

$$T \equiv t°C + 273.16 \qquad (1–10)$$

(such a scale will be referred to later as an *absolute temperature scale*, or the *kelvin* temperature scale, for historical reasons, with units of °K), the equation relating the state variables of a pure gas in the limit of indefinitely small pressures is

$$P\overline{V} = RT. \qquad (1–11)$$

Because of the original limitation $(P \to 0)$, this *equation of state* applies to what may be called an *ideal gas*. It is exact for this ideal, but is only approximate for any real gas (i.e., those for which $P \neq 0$). Nevertheless, as can be seen from Fig. 1–5, it represents the behavior quite well at small values of the pressure $(P \leq 1 \text{ atm})$.

The *ideal gas constant* R has a value which is independent of the nature of the gas. Its value is determined experimentally from measurements on real gases by the following mathematical prescription:

$$R = \lim_{P \to 0} \frac{P\overline{V}}{T} = 8.2057 \times 10^{-2} \text{ liter·atm/gm-mole·°K}. \qquad (1–12)$$

Other units may be found in which to express the ideal gas constant, but we shall deal with these later. From Eq. (1–12) we can determine the volume occupied by one gram-mole of an ideal gas at, say, 0°C and one atmosphere pressure. (These conditions are referred to frequently as *standard* conditions of *temperature* and *pressure*, or STP.) We obtain

$$\overline{V}_{\text{ideal}} = \frac{8.2057 \times 10^{-2} \text{ liter·atm/gm-mole·°K} \times 273.16°K}{1 \text{ atm}}$$

$$= 22.415 \text{ liter/gm-mole}.$$

To express the equation of state of a pure ideal gas in terms of the directly measurable quantities P, V, m, and T, we exhibit the following form:

$$PV = \frac{m}{W} RT. \tag{1-13}$$

3. THE IDEAL GAS

Because the equation of state of an ideal gas is a good approximation to the equation of state of a real gas at low values of its pressure, we can anticipate that certain of the properties of low-pressure gases will be almost identical with those of an ideal gas. In precise terms, the ideal gas is a limit (as $P \to 0$) of a real gas, so that the properties of an ideal gas are the limiting properties of real gases (as $P \to 0$).

A useful property of a gas is its *coefficient of isothermal compressibility*, β. This quantity refers to the relative change in volume produced in a fixed amount of gas when the pressure is altered under such conditions that the temperature is unaltered. Mathematically, we define

$$\beta = \mathop{-\lim}_{\substack{P' \to P, \ V' \to V \\ t \ \text{const}, \ m \ \text{const}}} \frac{1}{V} \left(\frac{V - V'}{P - P'} \right).$$

(The negative sign is introduced simply to conform to the *convention* that β be a positive quantity.) Since we may regard the volume of a pure gas as a function of its pressure, temperature, and mass, as in Eq. (1-5), we have from the definition of a partial derivative

$$\beta = -\frac{1}{V} \left(\frac{\partial V}{\partial P} \right)_{t,m} = -\frac{1}{v} \left(\frac{\partial v}{\partial P} \right)_{t}. \tag{1-14}$$

This is a general definition. For a pure ideal gas, we have from Eq. (1-13)

$$V = \frac{m}{W} \frac{RT}{P},$$

so that we obtain

$$\beta_{\text{ideal}} = \frac{1}{P}. \tag{1-15}$$

For an ideal gas, the isothermal compressibility coefficient is a function only of its pressure. Because of the inverse dependence upon the pressure, the compressibility coefficient can become enormous. At STP a liquid like mercury has an isothermal compressibility coefficient of 3.9×10^{-6}/atm. This property is an obvious one that, under ordinary conditions, distinguishes gases from liquids and solids.

Another useful property of a gas is its *coefficient of thermal expansion*, α. This quantity refers to the relative change in volume produced in a fixed amount of gas when the temperature is altered, but not the pressure. As previously, the mathematical definition now is

$$\alpha = \frac{1}{V}\left(\frac{\partial V}{\partial t}\right)_{P,m} = \frac{1}{v}\left(\frac{\partial v}{\partial t}\right)_P. \tag{1–16}$$

With Eqs. (1–10) and (1–13), we obtain for a pure ideal gas

$$\alpha_{\text{ideal}} = \frac{1}{T}. \tag{1–17}$$

The thermal coefficient of expansion of an ideal gas depends only upon its temperature. At room temperature, the relative change per degree in the volume of an ideal gas is thus approximately 1/300 or 0.33%. By comparison, at STP the thermal expansion coefficient for a liquid like mercury is approximately 0.018%/°C, which is considerably smaller. For a solid like silver, the corresponding value is approximately 0.0058%/°C. It is evident that gases at low pressures are also more "expandable" in a thermal sense than are solids or liquids. (However, the difference sometimes can be smaller than we have illustrated. For liquid acetone the value of α at STP is 0.13%/°C, suggesting a similarity in the behavior of liquids and gases which we shall examine shortly.)

For a real gas, α is found to depend on the pressure of the gas, although such dependence is slight. In addition, at atmospheric pressures one finds a slight variation in the value of α from one gas to another. Both of these facts must be kept in mind for later purposes, but will not be discussed further here.

So far, we have restricted our analysis to pure gases consisting of a single chemical species. The ideal gases we have referred to so far are limited also to pure gases. In order to extend the concept of an ideal gas, we consider now the following *conceptual experiment*. We imagine two different gases, each at the same pressure and temperature, confined in a vessel, as in Fig. 1–7(a), with a negligibly thin partition separating them. The partition is now removed and the gases are mixed thoroughly. We

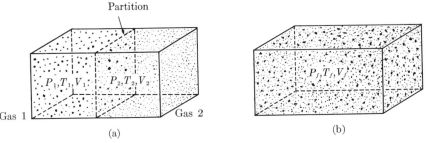

Fig. 1–7. Conceptual mixing of ideal gases. (a) Unmixed gases. (b) Mixed gases.

assume that no chemical changes occur under conditions of constant temperature. The final condition is indicated schematically in Fig. 1–7(b). The pressure of the gaseous mixture (which is homogeneous, since gases form homogeneous mixtures in all proportions of their constituents) is now measured. For real gases, the pressure is found to be very nearly the same as that originally present. As the initial pressures of the constituent gases get smaller and smaller, the difference also gets smaller. As a result, we conclude that the pressure of an *ideal gas mixture* is the same as that originally exhibited by the unmixed *ideal gases*. The process undergone by the gases can be summarized as follows:

$$T_{\text{final}} = T_{1,\text{initial}} = T_{2,\text{initial}},$$

$$P_{\text{final}} = P_{1,\text{initial}} = P_{2,\text{initial}},$$

$$V_{\text{final}} = V_{1,\text{initial}} + V_{2,\text{initial}},$$

where the subscripts 1, 2 refer to the constituents of the gas. Since no gas has been added to or removed from the total system, we also have for the numbers of gram-moles of gas

$$n_{\text{final}} = n_{1,\text{initial}} + n_{2,\text{initial}}.$$

The results which have been described are obtained for all values of the pressure, volume, temperature, and composition of an ideal gas mixture. Hence, we observe in general that

$$PV = nRT, \tag{1–18}$$

regardless of the composition of the ideal gas. All we need to know about the composition of the latter for its equation of state is the *total number* of gram-moles in the gas.

In general, a gaseous mixture of N constituents which do not react chemically will have a number n of gram-moles given by

$$n = n_1 + n_2 + \cdots + n_N = \sum_{i=1}^{N} n_i, \tag{1–19}$$

where each subscript refers to a distinct chemical species. For an ideal gaseous mixture, we can combine this equation with the previous one to obtain

$$P = \sum_{i=1}^{N} \left(\frac{n_i RT}{V} \right).$$

But the quantity $(n_i RT/V)$ is simply the pressure which the ith constituent would exert if it alone were in the volume V and had the temperature T.

This pressure is called the *partial pressure* of the constituent. Designating

$$\frac{n_i RT}{V} \equiv P_i, \tag{1–20}$$

we obtain

$$P = \sum_{i=1}^{N} P_i, \tag{1–21}$$

which expresses *Dalton's Law of Partial Pressures:* the total pressure of an ideal gaseous mixture is the sum of the partial pressures of the constituent gases.

While the relation we have derived appears to be in the nature of a mathematical definition, it can be tested experimentally. In particular, when one of the gases is a so-called *vapor* in equilibrium with a liquid, its partial pressure is equal to the *vapor pressure* of the liquid. The partial pressure of the residual gas can be found by subtracting the vapor pressure from the total pressure. Then, if we deal only with a binary mixture, Eq. (1–20) yields

$$\frac{P_1}{P_2} = \frac{P - P_2}{P_2} = \frac{n_1}{n_2},$$

where

$$P = P_1 + P_2$$

and P_2 is the vapor pressure in question. Measurements of n_1 and n_2 can be carried out by measuring the total mass of the gas, condensing out and weighing the vapor, and converting the latter, as well as that of the residue, to gram-moles. For real gases, the results are approximately in agreement with those predicted from ideal gas theory. Presumably, they will be in better agreement for gaseous mixtures at very small pressures.

A further useful property of an ideal gas mixture is that for specified values of pressure and temperature, the total volume of the mixture is the sum of the volumes of its constituents, at the same pressure and temperature. This behavior is approximately exhibited by real gases at ordinary pressures and temperatures. For ideal gases, we say that there is no volume change upon mixing. Mathematically, we have

$$V_{\text{final}}(T, P) = \sum_{i=1}^{N} V_i(T, P), \tag{1–22}$$

the compositional dependence being implicit. Because, for ideal gases at the same temperature and pressure, there is no volume change upon mixing (sometimes referred to simply as "volume of mixing"), a convenient way to indicate the composition of a mixture of ideal gases is to designate the volume fraction of each constituent. For each constituent i

$$V_i = \frac{n_i RT}{P}$$

so that, for any two constituents A and B,

$$\frac{V_A}{V_B} = \frac{n_A}{n_B}.$$

In an ideal gas mixture consisting of A, B, and C the mole fraction of A, say, is

$$x_A = \frac{n_A}{n_A + n_B + n_C} = \frac{V_A}{V_A + V_B + V_C} = \frac{V_A}{V_{\text{final}}}. \qquad (1\text{--}23)$$

An important use to which the equation of state of an ideal gas is put is to determine the molecular weight of a gas. From our discussion of ideal gas mixtures, we see that the total number of gram-moles is given by

$$\sum_{i=1}^{N} n_i = \frac{PV}{RT},$$

so that a determination of the mass of gas m corresponding to (T, P, V) permits a determination of the *mean molecular weight* of the gas mixture:

$$\overline{W} = \frac{m}{\sum_{i=1}^{N} n_i} = \frac{mRT}{PV} = \frac{RT}{Pv}. \qquad (1\text{--}24)$$

The quantities on the right-hand side of this equation are all measurable quantities for a given specimen of gas. If we wish to determine the molecular weight of a particular constituent in a mixture of ideal gas, we must use Eq. (1–20). For this purpose we must either measure directly or calculate the mass and the partial pressure of the constituent. In these terms, we have

$$W_i = \frac{m_i RT}{P_i V}. \qquad (1\text{--}25)$$

4. GASES AT HIGH PRESSURES

The behavior of a uniform gas at very low pressures leads, as we have seen, to a relatively simple relation between the variables of state of the gas. Because of the universal character of the relation, we have been led to the concept of an ideal gas. But real gases depart from the behavior expected from an ideal gas, and so we must examine the former in additional detail.

From the data of Table 1–2, or the graphs of Fig. 1–5, we observe that as the pressure of a gas increases so does its deviation from ideality. Moreover, the deviation is not always the same for every gas, nor even in the same sense. The deviations from the ideal gas equation of state at ordinary conditions are *positive* for hydrogen, but are sometimes *negative* for carbon monoxide. That is, $P\overline{V}/RT$ is greater than unity for hydrogen and less than unity for carbon monoxide. On the face of it, there seems to be no regularity in the deviations from ideality. Moreover, we must realize that one feature of real gases is completely absent in ideal gases: the phenomenon of *liquefaction*. Provided that the temperature of a chemically pure gas is less than a certain value which is characteristic of the gas, it is found that at sufficiently large pressure a gas *condenses* to form a liquid. This phenomenon is clearly not a property of an ideal gas! (In some instances, as exemplified by iodine, gases may condense to form solids. Such cases are not frequent for ordinary conditions, but conditions can always be found for any gas which will involve direct condensation to solids. We shall not explore this situation.)

In the process of condensation of a pure gas, one observes that a heterogeneous mixture is formed from the homogeneous gas and that the new *phase* formed is more dense. It is of interest to note how the variables of state are related when such a gas undergoes liquefaction. This is indicated in Fig. 1–8 for isopentane. It can be seen that as the specific volume of isopentane is made larger and larger, the pressure decreases. The limiting behavior at vanishingly small pressures becomes that of an ideal gas, which we have already considered. Focusing our attention on the lowest of the constant-temperature curves (called *isotherms*), we observe an increase in pressure as the volume decreases. This continues until a point is reached on the curve which connects the curve to a horizontal line on the P vs. v curve. In the region of volumes denoted by the horizontal line, the *pressure is constant*. This pressure is the *vapor pressure* of the liquid for the temperature in question. This same region corresponds to the heterogeneous mixture mentioned earlier. The total volume of one gram of isopentane varies between the values corresponding to the specific volume of the gas (at the pressure and temperature in question) and the specific volume of the liquid (at the same pressure and temperature). The specific volume of the heterogeneous mixture is expressible in terms of the fractions f of liquid and gas and the corresponding specific volumes. We have

$$v_{\text{mixture}} = f_{\text{gas}}v_{\text{gas}} + f_{\text{liq}}v_{\text{liq}}.$$

Having reached the point in the horizontal region corresponding to the smallest specific volume, we have a homogeneous system again. This time, however, it is pure liquid. Any attempt to decrease the specific

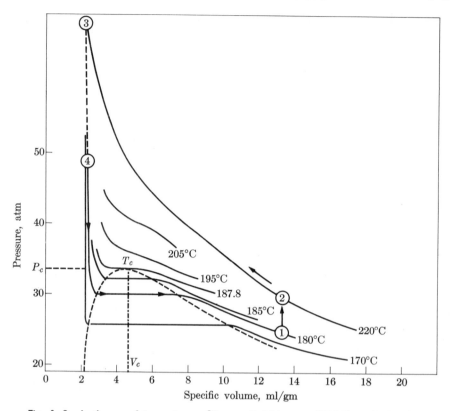

Fig. 1–8. Isotherms of isopentane. [Young, *Stoichiometry* (1918), p. 116. Cf. J. R. Partington, *An Advanced Treatise on Physical Chemistry*, Vol. I, p. 627. London: Longmans, Green and Company (1949).]

volume of the system now involves an extremely large increase in pressure. Since the coefficient of compressibility, Eq. (1–14), is simply related to the reciprocal of the slope of the P vs. v curve, one can appreciate that liquids have considerably smaller compressibilities than gases. It is to be noted that the heterogeneous mixture has an unlimited value (i.e., infinite) for the compressibility of the *system*.

The behavior which has been described can be seen to be duplicated for a variety of isotherms. Several of these are indicated in Fig. 1–8. However, as the temperature of the system is increased, a condition is achieved for which no horizontal region occurs. In such circumstances, there exists no heterogeneous region, regardless of the specific volume of the system. The lowest value of the temperature of the system for which no liquefaction is possible is called the *critical temperature* of the system. As can be seen from Fig. 1–8, the specific volumes of the liquid and gas at each temperature have values which approach each other as the critical temperature

TABLE 1–4

CRITICAL CONSTANTS OF SOME GASES*

Substance	t_C, °C	P_C, atm	ρ_C, gm/ml	$\dfrac{P_C \overline{V}_C}{R T_C}$
He	−267.9	2.26	0.0693	0.300
Ne	−228.7	25.9	0.484	0.297
Ar	−122	48	0.531	0.292
Kr	−63	54	0.78	0.336
Xe	16.6	58.2	1.155	0.277
H_2	−239.9	12.8	0.0310	0.304
N_2	−147.1	33.5	0.3110	0.293
O_2	−118.8	49.7	0.430	0.292
CO	−139	35	0.3110	0.286
CO_2	31.1	73.0	0.460	0.280
NO	−94	65	0.52	0.256

* Data from *Handbook of Chemistry and Physics.* Cleveland: Chemical Rubber Publishing Co.

is approached from below. The limiting value obtained for the specific volume as the critical temperature is approached is called the *critical volume* of the system. It corresponds to the volume at the maximum of the dotted curve in Fig. 1–8. The pressure corresponding to this point is termed the *critical pressure*. The critical values of pressure, temperature, and specified volume are listed for several gases in Table 1–4.

The critical phenomena which have been described imply an intimate connection between the liquid and gaseous states. Thus, we can start with a gas having state variables (P_1, v_1, T_1). Keeping v_1 fixed, we can raise the temperature to $T_2 > T_C$, where T_C is the critical temperature. During this change of temperature, no heterogeneity will have occurred in the system. The state of the system is designated by (P_2, v_1, T_2), which may now be altered at fixed temperature by decreasing the specific volume to $v_3 < v_C$, the latter corresponding to the critical volume. Again, no heterogeneity will have occurred. At the conclusion of the alteration, the state of the system is designated by (P_3, v_3, T_2). Consider next a decrease to the original temperature of the system at constant volume. The resulting state will be designated as (P_4, v_3, T_1) with $T_1 < T_C$. By design, the process may be selected to assure that no heterogeneity occurs. But if the specific volume is now increased at fixed temperature, the state of the system takes a path along an isotherm in which a heterogeneous region is traversed. The cycle of changes we have described is indicated in Fig. 1–8. We have contrived to return to the state (P_1, v_1, T_1) by means of a cyclic process, in the course of which a *single* transformation from liquid to gas has occurred. Because the liquid has been obtained from the gas as a result of changes involving no heterogeneous systems, it is evidently impossible to regard it as fundamentally different from the gas from which it was obtained. Lacking the final step of the previous cyclic process, we would have no evidence of any qualitative distinction between a gas and liquid.

Sometimes reference to a gas is made as follows. Above its critical temperature it is referred to as a *gas;* below its critical temperature it is referred to as a (condensable) *vapor* if the specific volume exceeds the critical volume. The liquid corresponds to those states for which both the temperature and volume are less than their critical values. A better term would seem to be *fluid* for all manifestations: liquid, vapor, or gas.

The importance of the phenomenon of liquefaction and critical behavior to our present interest—gases—lies in the implication that any general equation of state for a real gas must somehow relate as well to the liquid state. Because different liquid substances are not related to each other in a simple way, we may anticipate that there can be no simple, general equation of state for real gases. However, we shall obtain some which, although somewhat more complicated than that for an ideal gas, present a better approximation for real gases.

5. EQUATIONS OF STATE OF UNIFORM GASES—HIGH PRESSURES

As an illustration of the deviations in the behavior of a real gas from that expected from an ideal one, we have selected an isotherm of carbon dioxide and compared it with an isotherm for the ideal gas corresponding to it. This is shown in Fig. 1–9. One notes immediately the deviations of the real isotherm from the ideal gas isotherm. At very small values of the molal volume, the deviation is positive $[(P\overline{V}/RT) > 1]$, while at large values of the molal volume, the deviation is negative $[(P\overline{V}/RT) < 1]$. We have previously remarked that deviations from ideality occur for real gases under ordinary conditions and that these deviations may be either positive or negative, for different gases. Now we see that both sorts of deviations can occur in the same substance. Any equation of state of a general sort which may be constructed must exhibit this behavior.

A feature of some significance is to be noted in Fig. 1–8. The behavior at small values of the specific volume indicates a rather *abrupt* increase of pressure as the volume decreases to what seems to be some nonzero value. This nonzero value corresponds to the volume of the liquid. As a result, we might expect somewhat greater accuracy for pure gases at large pressures from an equation of state of the form

$$P(\overline{V} - \overline{V}_l) = RT, \qquad \overline{V} \rightarrow \overline{V}_l, \qquad (1–26)$$

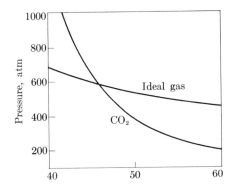

Fig. 1–9. Isotherms of CO_2 and ideal gas at 60°C. [Data from Amagat, Ann. Chim., **29**, 68 (1893).]

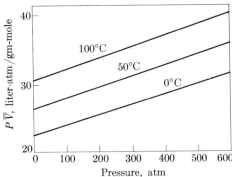

Fig. 1–10. Test of covolume equation of state for hydrogen. [Based upon compressibility data of Michels, Nijhoff, and Gerver, Ann. Phys., **12**, 562 (1932).]

where $\overline{V}_l$ refers to the molal volume of the liquid. Equation (1–26) is deceptively simple, since $\overline{V}_l$ is itself a function of pressure and temperature. However, because the coefficients of compressibility and thermal expansion (Section 3) are usually small for liquids, $\overline{V}_l$ will not change much in a restricted range of pressures and temperatures. It follows that Eq. (1–26) exhibits *only positive deviations* from ideality, so that it cannot adequately represent the behavior of real gases. However, since the negative deviations from ideality relate to liquefaction and the latter occurs only below the critical temperature, an equation of state of the form of Eq. (1–26) may be restricted to very large temperatures. The meaning to be attributed to $\overline{V}_l$ in such instances is that of an "effective liquid volume." It then is referred to as the *covolume* of the gas. A favorable system to test Eq. (1–26) at ordinary temperatures would seem to be hydrogen, because its critical temperature is so small (see Table 1–4). From Eq. (1–26) we should expect that

$$P\overline{V} = RT + P\overline{V}^*,$$

where $\overline{V}^*$ is now the covolume of the gas, to distinguish it from $\overline{V}_l$. Supposing that the covolume is constant and independent of pressure and temperature, we deduce that a plot of $(P\overline{V})$ vs. P should yield straight lines at each temperature. These lines should all have the same slope and intercepts, at $P = 0$, which are proportional to the absolute temperature. In Fig. 1–10, we have plotted some pertinent data for hydrogen. It can be seen that Eq. (1–26) is a good representation of the data. The slopes of all the curves are very nearly the same, as demanded by Eq. (1–26), but a very close examination would reveal a slight temperature dependence.

The value of $\overline{V}^*$ obtained is approximately 15.9 ml/gm-mole. The molal volume of hydrogen at its boiling point is 28.4 ml/gm-mole; its critical volume is 65.0 ml/gm-mole. The covolume of hydrogen thus has a value of approximately one-half the liquid volume at low temperatures, or about one-fourth the critical volume. Clearly, it must be regarded as an adjustable *parameter* in Eq. (1–26), its precise value depending upon the gas and, possibly, upon the temperature.

Nevertheless, the molecular basis of Eq. (1–26) is a reasonable one. At temperatures large compared with the critical temperature of the gas, the *free volume* of the gas (i.e., the volume diminished by a quantity of the order of the volume of the molecules) is to be used in an equation that otherwise appears to be similar to the equation of state of an ideal gas. The resulting equation of state involves, now, two parameters: R and $\overline{V}^*$, the former having a universal value for all gases, the latter having a value which depends upon the volume of the molecules of the gas. We may suppose that other gases will satisfy a covolume equation of state under the proper conditions, but we shall not elaborate this point here, in view of the limitations mentioned earlier (i.e., only positive deviations from ideality are accounted for). This is considered in Chapter 5.

It is necessary to deal with the behavior of pure gases under conditions proximate to liquefaction in order to emphasize any negative deviations from ideality. This can be assured if the temperature is less than the critical temperature of the gas. The negative deviations can be regarded as giving rise to an equation of state for pure real gases which predicts a pressure less than that expected from Eq. (1–26). Thus we can anticipate a more realistic equation of state, of the form

$$P = \frac{RT}{\overline{V} - \overline{V}^*} - F(\overline{V}, T), \qquad (1\text{–}27)$$

where $F(\overline{V}, T)$ is a function still to be determined. It is referred to as the *internal pressure* of the gas. [Note that Eq. (1–27) can be regarded as a *definition* of $F(\overline{V}, T)$ for real gases. Unless some specified form for this function is inserted in Eq. (1–27), the latter may be regarded as exact.] From the behavior exhibited by real gases, we must have

$$F(\overline{V}, T) > 0, \quad \text{all} \quad (\overline{V}, T) \qquad (1\text{–}28)$$

and

$$\lim_{\overline{V} \to \infty} F(\overline{V}, T) = 0. \qquad (1\text{–}29)$$

The first of these equations corresponds to an assumption that Eq. (1–26) contains all the positive deviations from ideality. The second equation is necessary to achieve ideality for any real gas at sufficiently small pressures. This restriction can be made sharper, however. Equation (1–27) can be rearranged to yield

$$\frac{P\overline{V}}{RT} = \frac{\overline{V}}{\overline{V} - \overline{V}^*} - \frac{\overline{V}}{RT} F(\overline{V}, T).$$

For the left side to approach unity as $\overline{V}$ increases indefinitely implies that

$$\lim_{\overline{V} \to \infty} \frac{\overline{V} F(\overline{V}, T)}{RT} = 0. \tag{1–30}$$

Hence, at fixed temperature and increasing molal volume of the gas, the internal pressure must approach zero more rapidly than a function which is inversely proportional to the molal volume.

Just as in the case of positive deviations from ideality, the negative deviations are related to the molecular structure of gases. In the former case, the deviations have been attributed to the covolume of the gas, which is related to the nonzero size of its constituent molecules. The positive deviations thus correspond to the strong repulsion which may be said to exist between molecules when the distance between them is made less than a certain minimum value.

Similarly, the negative deviations from ideality are attributable to attractive forces existing between gaseous molecules at somewhat larger intermolecular distances. There lies the molecular significance of Eq. (1–28). However, we can anticipate that, whatever the nature of these forces, they must ultimately be negligible for indefinitely large values of intermolecular distances. This is the molecular significance of Eq. (1–29) for the attractive forces. The corresponding behavior for repulsive forces is given automatically by the covolume equation of state, Eq. (1–26).

The determination of the internal pressure function $F(\overline{V}, T)$ from experimental data is possible in principle. However, the data do not permit a *simple* unique function to be determined. The reason for this may be traced to the discontinuous nature of the gas-liquid isotherm for temperatures smaller than the critical temperature of the substance. Any continuous differentiable function which may be found to represent the behavior of a gas at pressures less than the vapor pressure of the corresponding liquid must fail to do so at the vapor pressure and, hence, in the range of specific volumes corresponding to it. Viewed in another way, the function $F(\overline{V}, T)$ represents the negative deviations from ideality. As we have already seen and incorporated into the covolume equation of state, Eq. (1–26), the positive deviations overwhelm the negative deviations at sufficiently small values of the specific volume. For sufficiently large values of the specific volume, the negative deviations (as well as the positive ones) vanish rapidly, as indicated by Eq. (1–30). Thus, only at intermediate values of the specific volume can an appreciable effect be observed due to the negative deviations. This region corresponds to the

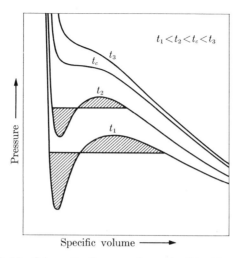

Fig. 1–11. Schematic diagram of van der Waals' equation.

liquefaction region, or close to it, where no continuous differentiable function can be correct at temperatures below the critical value.

In spite of these difficulties, a variety of functions has been suggested for the internal pressure. At temperatures which are not large compared with the critical temperatures, these functions represent the behavior of gases considerably more accurately than does Eq. (1–26). Historically, one of the earliest satisfactory approximations was given in 1873 by J. D. van der Waals. (He arrived at it from a simplified theoretical argument, which we will not reproduce here.) It is

$$P = \frac{RT}{\overline{V} - b} - \frac{a}{\overline{V}^2}.$$ (1–31)

The quantities a and b are assumed to be positive constants characteristic of each pure gas, i.e., parameters, with the quantity b corresponding to the covolume, as we already have seen. It is evident that Eq. (1–30) is satisfied. A schematic plot of Eq. (1–31) is given in Fig. 1–11 for several temperatures. The inadequacy just discussed is evident: no heterogeneous region is in evidence. (Compare with Fig. 1–8.) The inadequacy is emphasized even more strongly from the mathematical standpoint when we notice that the function in Eq. (1–31) allows the possibility of *negative pressures* for sufficiently small values of the temperature.

These inadequacies can be circumvented by restricting the applicability of van der Waals' equation to certain ranges of values of the molal volume. In order to simulate the actual isotherm of a gas (Fig. 1–8), we may suppose that a constant pressure line can be erected to connect the region which lies to the left of the minimum and the region which lies to the right of the maximum. This is indicated in Fig. 1–11. But where to place the horizontal line? The answer to this question was given by Clerk Maxwell. On the basis of a thermodynamic argument, he pointed out that the horizontal line must be constructed so that the areas enclosed between it and the van der Waals equation, one area lying above and the other below the line, are equal. These areas are indicated in Fig. 1–11 by crosshatching. The resulting isotherm then consists of the two portions which are given by Eq. (1–31) and the horizontal line connecting them. The excluded portion of the van der Waals equation of state relates to nonequilibrium or *metastable* states of the system.

The thermodynamic argument used by Maxwell is a very simple one. Supposing that a system could be made to traverse a path of decreasing volume along an isotherm given by van der Waals' equation (or any other, for that matter), we should have a continuous isothermal transformation from gas to liquid. If we make certain to start and end up with the same value of the pressure and if we pick the pressure to correspond to the vapor pressure of the liquid, we may return to the initial gaseous condition via the heterogeneous region, corresponding to the horizontal line. Both these paths may be regarded as reversible paths. As a result, we have a cyclic reversible isothermal path which, according to the Second Law of Thermodynamics, can have no net work associated with it. But the net work done is simply proportional to the sum of the areas enclosed by the equation of state and the vapor pressure line. Hence the criterion stated follows.

TABLE 1–5

VAN DER WAALS CONSTANTS AND NORMAL BOILING
CONSTANTS FOR VARIOUS GASES*

Substance	$a, \dfrac{1^2 \cdot atm}{(gm\text{-mole})^2}$	$b, \dfrac{liter}{gm\text{-mole}}$	$t_b, °C$	$\overline{V}_b, \dfrac{liter}{gm\text{-mole}}$
He	0.03412	0.02370	−263	0.0328
Ne	0.2107	0.01709	−246	0.0167
Ar	1.345	0.03219	−187	0.0283
Kr	2.318	0.03978	−146	0.0323
Xe	4.194	0.05105	−109	0.0430
H_2	0.2444	0.02661	−253	0.0285
N_2	1.390	0.03913	−196	0.0348
O_2	1.360	0.03183	−183	0.0281
CO	1.485	0.03985	−190	0.0354
CO_2	3.592	0.04267	—	—
NO	1.340	0.02789	—	—

* Data from *Handbook of Chemistry and Physics*. Cleveland: Chemical Rubber Publishing Co.

TABLE 1–6

RELATIVE VAN DER WAALS CONSTANTS FOR HELIUM AT
VARIOUS TEMPERATURES*

Temperature, °K	a (relative)	b (relative)
15–21	+1 (ref. value)	1 (ref. value)
90–123	+0.61	0.89
173–223	−0.11	0.78
223–273	−0.70	0.74
323–373	−2.54	0.61
473–573	−4.70	0.52
573–673	−4.20	0.54

* Adapted from P. Weiss, *Jubile de M. Brillouin*, Paris
(1936). Cf. J. Frankel, *Kinetic Theory of Liquids*, p. 187.
New York: Dover Publications, Inc. (1955).

While the van der Waals equation of state as modified in the liquefaction
region is a good representation of gaseous behavior, it is only approximate.
The parameters a and b have to be determined by fitting the van der Waals
equation to the actual behavior of gases. Some values for pure gases, so
determined, are given in Table 1–5. The molal volumes of the liquids at
the normal boiling point are given also. However, these values represent
some sort of "best" values. (Actually, they have been computed from
values of the critical temperature and pressure, discussed in the following
section.) A more precise fitting would disclose that both a and b vary
with temperature, a feature which was not inherent in the original deduc-
tion by van der Waals. This is illustrated in Table 1–6, for helium. Note
that a ultimately changes sign at sufficiently large temperatures, suggesting
that the covolume equation of state cannot ultimately account for the
positive deviations from ideality.

Numerous modifications of van der Waals' equation of state, along with
the modification that more realistically deals with the liquefaction region,
have been suggested. A pair of these, which have only two parameters
requiring determination from experimental data, are given here. First,
we have an equation due to D. Berthelot,

$$P = \frac{RT}{\overline{V} - b} - \frac{a}{T\overline{V}^2},$$ (1–32)

where some attempt is made to separate out the temperature dependence
in van der Waals' a. This equation does not give reliable results, because
it apparently overcorrects the temperature dependence. (Note that the

parameters in Berthelot's equation are not numerically the same as those in van der Waals'.) Second, an equation due to Dieterici has a markedly different form:

$$P = \frac{RT}{\overline{V} - b} e^{-a/RT\overline{V}}. \tag{1-33}$$

For large values of $\overline{V}$, the exponent is small. Hence, making use of the exponential series,

$$e^{-X} = 1 - X + \frac{X^2}{2} - \frac{X^3}{6} + \cdots = \sum_{n=0}^{\infty} \frac{(-X)^n}{n!},$$

we have as an approximation for $(a/RT\overline{V}) \ll 1$:

$$e^{-a/RT\overline{V}} \doteq 1 - \frac{a}{RT\overline{V}},$$

where $(\doteq)$ means "approximately equal to." With this approximation

$$P \doteq \frac{RT}{\overline{V} - b} - \frac{a}{\overline{V}(\overline{V} - b)},$$

which reduces to van der Waals' equation for conditions such that $\overline{V} \gg b$. (Here, again, the parameters of Dieterici's equation are not numerically identical with those of van der Waals. However, it can be expected that they will be rather close to them in value.)

There is no reason to suppose that two parameters in an equation of state of a pure gas are sufficient to represent gaseous behavior adequately. Many equations of state have been suggested in which more than two parameters appear. These equations permit better adjustment to the data than is possible with only two parameters. However, we shall not exhibit them. We shall simply take note of a general form of the equation of state of a pure gas—a form which is useful for theoretical purposes. It is the *virial equation* of state:

$$P\overline{V} = RT + \frac{B(T)}{\overline{V}} + \frac{C(T)}{\overline{V}^2} + \cdots \tag{1-34}$$

The quantities RT, $B(T)$, $C(T)$, etc., are referred to as the first, second, third, etc., *virial coefficients*. In these terms the van der Waals equation can be presented in a virial form. Since for $(b/\overline{V}) < 1$,

$$\frac{1}{\overline{V} - b} = \frac{1}{\overline{V}} \left(\frac{1}{1 - b/\overline{V}} \right) = \frac{1}{\overline{V}} \left(1 + \frac{b}{\overline{V}} + \frac{b^2}{\overline{V}^2} + \cdots \right) = \sum_{n=0}^{\infty} \frac{b^n}{\overline{V}^{n+1}},$$

we have for a van der Waals gas

$$P\overline{V} = RT + \frac{(RTb - a)}{\overline{V}} + RT \sum_{n=2}^{\infty} \frac{b^n}{\overline{V}^n}. \qquad (1\text{–}35)$$

For sufficiently large values of $\overline{V}$, only the first two terms on the right-hand side of the equation need be retained.

With this approximation, we notice that there exists a temperature, called the *Boyle temperature*, T_B, for which the ideal gas equation is satisfied at small, but nonzero, values of the pressure. (From Fig. 1–5, CO at 50°C satisfies the ideal gas equation for pressures of less than 50 atmospheres.) Stated differently, the slope of the $P\overline{V}$ vs. P curve is zero at the origin. This occurs in general when the second virial coefficient vanishes. For the van der Waals gas, this occurs at

$$T_B = \frac{a}{bR}. \qquad (1\text{–}36)$$

Above the Boyle temperature, gases at small pressures exhibit positive deviations from ideality; below the Boyle temperature, negative deviations are exhibited under the same conditions of pressure. This is in accord with the general properties of real gases, and is not dependent upon an exact knowledge of the equation of state.

For real gases at small pressures, use of the ideal gas equation to determine the molecular weight is generally in error. The actual behavior of a real gas at small pressures is illustrated in Fig. 1–12 for temperatures greater than, equal to, and less than the Boyle temperature. From the first two terms of Eq. (1–34), a good approximation is

$$PV \doteq \left(\frac{m}{W}\right) RT + \left(\frac{m}{W}\right)^2 \frac{B(T)}{V}, \qquad (1\text{–}37)$$

or, rearranging, we obtain

$$\left(\frac{W}{m}\right)^2 PV - \left(\frac{W}{m}\right) RT - \frac{B(T)}{V} \doteq 0. \qquad (1\text{–}38)$$

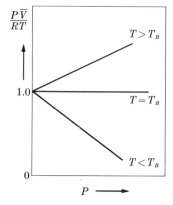

Fig. 1–12. Behavior of $P\overline{V}/RT$ for real gases at low pressures.

This equation is quadratic in (W/m) and can be solved in explicit form. Only the positive sign has meaning, since for $P \to 0$ we must obtain the ideal gas result, and so we obtain

$$\frac{W}{m} \doteq \frac{RT + \sqrt{(RT)^2 + 4PB(T)}}{2PV}. \qquad (1\text{–}39)$$

Under conditions such that ideal behavior is a good approximation, we may set

$$4PB(T) \ll (RT)^2$$

and exploit the expansion

$$\sqrt{1 + X} = 1 + \tfrac{1}{2}X - \tfrac{1}{8}X^2 + \cdots.$$

Then we obtain

$$W \doteq \frac{mRT}{PV}\left[1 + \frac{PB(T)}{(RT)^2}\right], \tag{1–40}$$

from which the molecular weight W can be evaluated in terms of measured values of P, V, T, and m if $B(T)$ is known. For the van der Waals gas, $B(T)$ can be estimated from Eq. (1–35) and Table 1–5. The quantity mRT/PV can be recognized as the *molecular weight computed from the ideal gas equation of state*. When $B(T)$ is positive, corresponding to positive deviations from ideality, the actual molecular weight exceeds the previous value; when $B(T)$ is negative, the actual molecular weight is less than the ideal gas value.

For mixtures of real gases, the properties are not as simply related to the pure real gases as in the case of ideal gases. This complexity is evident from the observation that the condensation of gaseous mixtures, with only rare exceptions, yields liquids which differ from them in composition. Nevertheless, various rules have been proposed for using a van der Waals equation of state for binary mixtures. Perhaps the simplest of these is worth presenting. If the gas consists of n_1 gram-moles of one pure gas and n_2 gram-moles of a second pure gas, then

$$\overline{V} = \frac{V}{n_1 + n_2}$$

and Eq. (1–31) is to be used for the mixture, with

$$a = (a_1^{1/2}x_1 + a_2^{1/2}x_2)^2, \tag{1–31a}$$

and

$$b = b_1 x_1 + b_2 x_2. \tag{1–31b}$$

Here the subscript refers to the individual pure gas and x is its mole fraction. [The additivity rule expressed in Eq. (1–31b) seems plausible in the light of a direct relation between molecular size and covolumes. The previous equation is quite arbitrary.] For real gases, as exemplified by the van der Waals gas, no simple law of partial pressures, Eq. (1–21), obtains. Neither can one conclude that there is no volume of mixing as given by Eq. (1–22).

6. CRITICAL PHENOMENA AND CORRESPONDING STATES

The critical phenomena exhibited by pure real gases *suggests* that at their critical points different gases are somehow quite similar. Just how similar remains to be seen. In Table 1–4, we note that the values of $(P_C V_C / R T_C)$ vary somewhat from substance to substance. Clearly, quantitatively precise similarity should demand identical values for all gases, so that any quantitative similarity relation we seek between different gases is only an approximate one.

Nevertheless, a notion of similarity finds confirmation through an equation of state like van der Waals'. To establish the extent of similar behavior, we express the condition corresponding to the critical point in mathematical terms. Since the critical point is the limit of the horizontal regions in the equations of state, it follows that the slope of the isotherm at the critical point is

$$\left(\frac{\partial P}{\partial \overline{V}}\right)_T = 0 \quad \text{at} \quad T = T_C, \quad \overline{V} = \overline{V}_C. \tag{1–41}$$

This behavior is indicated in Fig. 1–11. In general, it can be shown that a *stable* state of a system is one for which $(\partial P / \partial \overline{V})_T \leq 0$. (The argument that leads to this conclusion is a thermodynamic one of general validity, but we will not give it here. It corresponds to the statement that systems which are squeezed at constant temperature cannot expand if they are in a stable condition. This result is the thermodynamic reason why the *entire* van der Waals equation of state cannot correspond to a stable system.) But then it must follow that the critical point is an extreme value of $(\partial P / \partial \overline{V})_T$, so that it also must be a point of inflection. That is,

$$\left(\frac{\partial^2 P}{\partial \overline{V}^2}\right)_T = 0 \quad \text{at} \quad T = T_C, \quad \overline{V} = \overline{V}_C. \tag{1–42}$$

Applying Eqs. (1–41) and (1–42) to the van der Waals equation of state, we obtain

$$\frac{R T_C}{(\overline{V}_C - b)^2} = \frac{2a}{\overline{V}_C^3} \tag{1–43}$$

and

$$\frac{2 R T_C}{(\overline{V}_C - b)^3} = \frac{6a}{\overline{V}_C^4}. \tag{1–44}$$

Dividing the first of these equations by the second, we obtain

$$\tfrac{1}{2}(\overline{V}_C - b) = \tfrac{1}{3}\overline{V}_C$$

or

$$\overline{V}_C = 3b. \tag{1–45}$$

Substitution of this result into Eq. (1–43) yields

$$T_C = \frac{2a(\overline{V}_C - b)^2}{\overline{V}_C^3 R} = \frac{8a}{27bR}. \tag{1–46}$$

These results may be substituted into Eq. (1–31), with the result that

$$P_C = \frac{a}{27b^2}. \tag{1–47}$$

Equations (1–45) through (1–47) express the critical values of the state variables in terms of a and b. Conversely, we have

$$a = 3P_C\overline{V}_C^2, \qquad b = \tfrac{1}{3}\overline{V}_C,$$

as well as other relations that can be derived from the result that we must also have, upon combining Eqs. (1–45) through (1–47),

$$\frac{P_C\overline{V}_C}{RT_C} = \frac{3}{8} = 0.375. \tag{1–48}$$

A comparison with Table 1–4 shows that although any van der Waals gas gives a constant value of $(P_C\overline{V}_C/RT_C)$, this value is quite a bit larger than the values observed experimentally.

Somewhat better agreement with experiment is achieved with Dieterici's equation of state, Eq. (1–33). By carrying out the previous analysis, one finds that

$$\overline{V}_C = 2b,$$

$$P_C = \frac{a}{4e^2b^2}, \qquad e = 2.718282,$$

$$T_C = \frac{a}{4bR}.$$

With these values,

$$(P_C V_C/RT_C) = (2/e^2) = 0.2708,$$

a value which is considerably closer to the experimental values than is the van der Waals value. For this reason alone, we should favor the Dieterici equation.

Nevertheless, the van der Waals equation may be used to illustrate a *Corresponding States Relation*. With elimination of a and b in the van der Waals equation, we obtain the following:

$$\left(P + \frac{a}{\overline{V}^2}\right)(\overline{V} - b) = RT = \left(P + \frac{3P_C\overline{V}_C^2}{\overline{V}^2}\right)(\overline{V} - \tfrac{1}{3}\overline{V}_C).$$

With rearrangement, we obtain further

$$\left\{\left(\frac{P}{P_C}\right) + 3\left(\frac{\overline{V}_C}{\overline{V}}\right)^2\right\}\left\{\left(\frac{\overline{V}}{\overline{V}_C}\right) - \frac{1}{3}\right\} = \frac{RT}{P_C V_C} = \frac{8}{3}\left(\frac{T}{T_C}\right).$$

This form suggests that pressure, volume, and temperature should be measured in terms of ratios with respect to the critical values. We define the *reduced variables* of state

$$\pi \equiv \frac{P}{P_C}, \qquad \phi \equiv \frac{\overline{V}}{\overline{V}_C}, \qquad \vartheta \equiv \frac{T}{T_C}.$$

Then, in terms of the reduced variables, van der Waals' *reduced equation* of state becomes

$$\left(\pi + \frac{3}{\phi^2}\right)(3\phi - 1) = 8\vartheta, \qquad\qquad (1\text{–}49)$$

an equation that is remarkable in containing no arbitrary parameters. This is possible, of course, in terms of the appropriate pressure, volume, and temperature scales.

For completeness, the reduced equation of state of Dieterici will be given. It is

$$\pi = \frac{\vartheta}{2\phi - 1}\, e^{2 - (2/\vartheta\phi)}.$$

The Corresponding States Relation, illustrated by Eq. (1–49), is a general result for all appropriate two-parameter equations of state which exhibit a critical point. Stated more precisely, any equation of state which can be rendered in a reduced form and which exhibits a critical point can have no more than two parameters characteristic of each gas. To see this, we represent the equation of state (in nonreduced form) by

$$P = P(\overline{V}, RT, C_1, C_2).$$

Application of Eqs. (1–38) and (1–39) yields two equations which permit the two constants to be determined in terms of P_C, V_C, RT_C. Since, by hypothesis, the equation of state can be converted to a reduced form, it follows that the constants can be eliminated. When more than two constants occur, the critical point does not permit their values to be determined uniquely.

A variety of tests can be made of the Corresponding States Relation which do not require a knowledge of the equation of state. A constant value of $P_C V_C/RT_C$ is one of them and, as we have seen, it is satisfied only approximately. Another test of this relation can be made by comparing the reduced volume of various liquids at a fixed value of the reduced pressure. If the Corresponding States Relation is precise, the result should

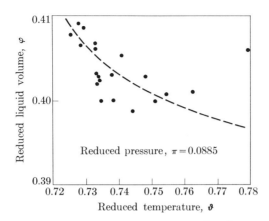

Fig. 1–13. Plot of reduced volumes vs. reduced temperature, for various substances at fixed reduced pressure. [Data tabulated in J. R. Partington, *An Advanced Treatise on Physical Chemistry*, Vol. I, p. 695. London: Longmans, Green and Company (1949).]

be a single curve of ϕ vs. ϑ. This is shown in Fig. 1–13, where each point represents a different substance. Marked deviations do occur, but there can be little doubt that a Corresponding States Relation is more than just a crude approximation. However, since it is not satisfied in a precise sense, we must look to equations of state containing more than two adjustable parameters for a more precise description of gaseous behavior. However, this will not be done here, since all the essential molecular features of gaseous behavior can be incorporated in two-parameter equations of state. Instead, we shall turn to an examination of other properties of gases which will illuminate their molecular constitution.

7. SUMMARY

Starting with the state variables of a uniform gas: pressure, volume, temperature, mass, and composition, we have reviewed the means by which they are measured and the terms in which they are expressed. Emphasizing the experimental behavior of gases at low pressures, the equation of state of an ideal gas has been obtained as a summary of the laws of Boyle, Charles, and Avogadro. The properties of ideal gas mixtures have been examined.

Gases at high pressures have been considered. Especially important are the deviations from ideality as they are manifest in the vicinity of liquefaction. Critical phenomena have been described and the existence of a fundamental relation between liquids and gases has been inferred. Equations of state for real gases include a covolume correction, corresponding to the nonzero size of their constituent molecules. This correction provides for positive deviations from ideality. Negative deviations are provided for in an approximate, semiquantitative way by introducing an internal pressure function. The equation of van der Waals has been examined as a representation of the behavior of real gases. Other equations of state have been noted. The relation between the reduced variables of state and the general concept of Corresponding States has been examined.

EXERCISES

1. Using Eqs. (1–46) and (1–47) and the data of Table 1–4, evaluate the van der Waals constants. Compare with the values in Table 1–5. (The values of the critical pressure and temperature are more easily obtained than is the value of the critical density. Hence these values are usually employed.)

2. The Dieterici constants are very similar to the van der Waals constants. Using the values of the critical pressure and temperature show that

$$a \text{ (Dieterici)} = 1.284a \text{ (van der Waals)},$$
$$b \text{ (Dieterici)} = 1.083b \text{ (van der Waals)}.$$

3. Derive the following values of the critical pressure, temperature and molal volume for a Berthelot gas in terms of its parameters:

$$\overline{V}_C = 3b,$$
$$P_C = \sqrt{aR/216b^3},$$
$$T_C = \sqrt{8a/27bR}.$$

Show that Eq. (1–48) is satisfied by a Berthelot gas.

4. Assuming that the gases obey van der Waals' equation of state, determine the error made in using the ideal gas equation of state to determine the molecular weight at STP of (a) hydrogen, (b) nitrogen, and (c) carbon dioxide.
   Answers: (a) −0.070%;   (b) +0.10%;   (c) +0.53%.

5. A certain gas has the following densities at 0°C:

P, atm	0.2	0.4	0.6	0.8
m/V, gm/liter	0.5336	1.0790	1.6363	2.2054

Determine (a) the accurate molecular weight of the gas and (b) the second virial coefficient of the gas.
   Answers: (a) 59.14 gm/gm-mole;   (b) −26.72 $1^2 \cdot$ atm/(gm-mole)^2.

6. (a) Verify that the Boyle temperature for a Dieterici gas satisfies Eq. (1–35) and determine (T_B/T_C) for such a gas.
   (b) Determine the corresponding value for a van der Waals gas.
   Answers: (a) 4;   (b) 3.375.

7. Using the van der Waals constants for carbon dioxide in Table 1–5, calculate the pressure for a density of 0.516 gm/ml at a temperature of $-16.5°C$. *Answer:* Approximately zero atmosphere.

8. The density of dry air at STP is 1.2929 gm/liter. Assuming that it may be treated as an ideal gas and that it consists entirely of oxygen and nitrogen, determine (a) the mean molecular weight and (b) the composition of air. (c) Assuming that it may be treated as a van der Waals gas, estimate the error in the computed molecular weight.
   Answers: (a) 28.98 gm/gm-mole; (b) 24.5 mole percent oxygen (note!); (c) $+0.12\%$.

9. Evaluate the ratios (T_b/T_C) for the gases listed in Tables 1–4 and 1–5 and determine whether these values support a "corresponding-states" relation for the normal boiling points of liquids. Suggest how such a relation may be obtained in empirical terms.
   Answer: Try plotting (T_b/T_C) versus P_C.

10. The *internal pressure* of a fluid may be *defined* as

$$P_{\text{int}} = T \left(\frac{\partial P}{\partial T} \right)_{\overline{V}} - P.$$

   Determine the expression for (a) the van der Waals gas and (b) the Dieterici gas. Evaluate the internal pressure at the critical point for (c) the van der Waals gas and (d) the Dieterici gas.
   Answers: (a) $\dfrac{a}{\overline{V}^2}$; (b) $\dfrac{a}{\overline{V}(\overline{V} - b)} e^{-a/RT\overline{V}}$; (c) $3Pc$; (d) $2Pc$.

11. Evaluate $(1/P)(\partial P/\partial T)_{\overline{V}}$ for (a) an ideal gas, (b) a van der Waals gas, and (c) a Dieterici gas.
   Answers: (a) $\dfrac{1}{T}$; (b) $\dfrac{1}{T}\left(1 + \dfrac{a}{P\overline{V}^2}\right)$; (c) $\dfrac{1}{T}\left(1 + \dfrac{a}{RT\overline{V}}\right)$.

12. Carbon dioxide at STP yields a value of $0.003724/°C$ for $(1/P)(\partial P/\partial T)_{\overline{V}}$. The density of CO_2 at STP is 1.9769 gm/liter. (a) Use these values to estimate a (Exercise 11) for CO_2. (Note that no substantial difference exists between a van der Waals gas and a Dieterici gas at STP.) (b) Use the value of a obtained to estimate b from van der Waals' equation.
   Answers: (a) 8.65 $l^2 \cdot \text{atm}/(\text{gm-mole})^2$; (b) 0.324 liter/gm-mole.

2 · PROPERTIES OF NONUNIFORM GASES

1. BEHAVIOR OF NONUNIFORM GASES

The properties of uniform gases which have been considered thus far are essentially *static* properties of these substances. In the absence of chemical reactivity, which we have assumed tacitly, no changes in the state of such a gas will occur with the passing of time. Later, when we examine the behavior of uniform gases from a molecular point of view, we will find that properties like the pressure and temperature are, in fact, related to the *dynamical properties* of the molecules comprising the gases. The essentially static character of the *macroscopic state* of a uniform gas is not to be denied, however. (It is only this sort of state we are dealing with at present. While the molecular constitution of a gas is acknowledged, it is done so in a minimal way which avoids dealing with the dynamical properties of molecules.)

In general, the values of the intensive variables of a nonuniform gas—pressure, density, temperature, chemical composition—will, at the same instant of time, vary from one region to another in the gas, as in Fig. 1–1. In the limiting situation referred to in Chapter 1, a nonuniform gas may be regarded as the composite of an indefinitely large number of connected regions of arbitrarily small size and extent. Each region is uniform. The state variables of a nonuniform gas thus can be seen to be functions of the *position* within the gas, since any region to which these variables pertain can be specified by its spatial location. As a simplification, with no great restriction on generality, we may regard these variables as continuous and differentiable functions of position. If the cartesian coordinates of a point within a gas are (x, y, z), we suppose that at any instant of time t

$$P = P(x, y, z, t), \qquad v = v(x, y, z, t), \qquad T = T(x, y, z, t), \text{ etc.} \quad (2\text{–}1)$$

In the case of gaseous mixtures, the composition also will be assumed to be a function of position and time. Furthermore, we shall suppose that these functions have derivatives of all orders with respect to the coordinates. At any position in space, and at each instant of time, we may suppose that certain relations exist between the variables of state: the relations may be those which we have discussed for uniform gases, or others if necessary. A (macroscopic) *state of a nonuniform gas* requires

40

the simultaneous specification of the previous functions at all positions and times. In these terms, the (macroscopic) *states of a uniform gas* are particular ones of the possible states of a nonuniform gas. Mathematically, they correspond to those for which

$$\left(\frac{\partial P}{\partial x}\right)_{y,z,t} = \left(\frac{\partial P}{\partial y}\right)_{x,z,t} = \left(\frac{\partial P}{\partial z}\right)_{x,y,t} = 0, \quad \text{for all } (x, y, z, t), \quad (2\text{–}2)$$

with similar conditions for all the other intensive variables. The possibility that these variables for a uniform gas may depend upon time is not precluded, but we have had no need to consider it explicitly.

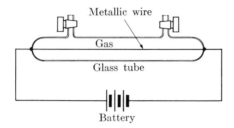

Fig. 2–1. Apparatus for heat conduction.

When nonuniform gases are examined in the laboratory, it is found that with the passage of time changes often occur in their macroscopic states (as described above). However, certain nonuniform states are possible which are *stationary* in time. These are achievable in the presence of certain external influences upon the gas. The simplest of these conditions, perhaps, is the one resulting from the earth's gravitational action upon a long, vertical column of gas. Even though the temperature of the gas is uniform, the pressure and density at each point will nevertheless vary with the height of the point. (A corresponding situation occurs also in liquids, and so the pressure in the sea varies markedly with the depth below the surface.) As we shall see in Chapter 4, this condition is entirely understandable as an *equilibrium* condition which is determined by *static* external forces acting upon the gaseous system. More pertinent to our present interest is the example of a nonuniform state of a gas which is obtained by maintaining two different regions at fixed but different temperatures. This condition can be obtained in the laboratory by enclosing a gas in a thin, narrow glass tube through the axis of which passes a thin metallic wire, as indicated in Fig. 2–1. The thin glass tube can be kept at constant temperature by maintaining it in contact with a thermostat. The wire is maintained at a different temperature by passing an electric current through it. The state of the nonuniform gas is maintained only by a flow of *heat* through it. Hence, while the situation we have described is static in appearance, the flows of electrical current and heat make the over-all system of gas and surroundings certainly nonstatic. Nevertheless, the state of the gas is *stationary* and corresponds to the mathematical condition that

$$\left(\frac{\partial P}{\partial t}\right)_{x,y,z} = \left(\frac{\partial v}{\partial t}\right)_{x,y,z} = \left(\frac{\partial T}{\partial t}\right)_{x,y,z} = 0, \quad \text{for all } (x, y, z, t). \quad (2\text{–}3)$$

The flow of *heat* associated with temperature differences between different regions of substances, including gases, requires some comment. From the First Law of Thermodynamics, a flow of heat is related to the energy changes which occur in a system, and the work which may be involved. In the case of a stationary state, the energy of the *system* remains constant as a function of time. Consequently, the flow of heat is simply equated to the work done upon the system in such cases. In the present example, the expressed equivalence between work and heat enables us to *calculate* the heat flow by calculating the electrical work done by the passage of electrical current through the wire while the temperature of the wire is kept constant. The electrical work in the present steady-state experiment is simply the product of the electrical charge and the electrical potential (difference) through which it is transferred. The electrical charge is the product of the stationary current and the time interval over which it is transferred. The *rate* of electrical work, and thus the rate of heat flow, is constant under the stated conditions, and equal to the product of the electrical potential and current.

A more *direct measurement* of the heat flow can be made however. If the thermostat surrounding the apparatus in Fig. 2–1 consists of a heterogeneous mixture of solid and liquid phases of a pure substance in equilibrium (e.g., ice and liquid water at a temperature of 0°C, or solid and liquid phases of acetic acid at 16.6°C), the temperature of the thin glass tube will be maintained at a constant value for as long as two phases coexist. The amount of solid phase in an otherwise isolated mixture will depend upon the amount of heat it has received since its preparation. This conclusion follows from the fact that the amount of heat which must be supplied to melt a specified quantity of solid at its melting point is proportional to the mass of the solid. The ratio of these two quantities is the *latent heat of fusion*, which is an *intensive* property of the solid. As a result, a measurement of the mass of solid in the mixture permits the heat received by the thermostat to be calculated. The latter quantity, in turn, is seen to be equal to that originally supplied by the heated wire. The principle of operation described for the measurement of heat is incorporated in the *Bunsen calorimeter*.

For future reference, we note here the unit frequently employed for designating thermal energies. It is the *normal calorie*, defined as the amount of (heat) energy required to raise the temperature of one gram of water at atmospheric pressure from 14.5°C to 15.5°C. In terms of ordinary mechanical units,

$$1 \approx 4.1855 \times 10^7 \text{ ergs/calorie.}$$

Examples of nonstationary behavior are more commonly found in nonuniform gases. In terms of the previous illustration, a sudden alteration of the temperature of the inner wire results in an alteration of the intensive variables at every point within the gas, which alteration continues in time. Equation (2–3) no longer is satisfied. If the new temperature is held fixed, a new steady-state condition is reached after the lapse of a sufficiently long interval of time, i.e., asymptotically from a mathematical point of view, but *finite* from a practical viewpoint. At such a time, Eq. (2–3) again obtains. Another example of nonstationary behavior is to be found in the *diffusive mixing* of gases. Two different gases at the same pressure and temperature, as in Fig. 1–7(a), require simply the removal of the separator to yield the ultimate condition represented by Fig. 1–7(b). *No stirrers or other mixing devices need be provided.* The gases are said to diffuse through each other. Under the stated conditions, the ultimate condition of the gases is a uniform mixture.

The properties we have mentioned are illustrative of the so-called *transport* properties of gases. Since, as we shall see later, these properties are closely connected with the molecular constitution of gases, we will examine certain of them more closely in this chapter.

2. THERMAL CONDUCTIVITY IN GASES

The passage of heat through a gas is usually accompanied by changes in the temperature of each region of the gas. However, as already mentioned, experimental arrangements are possible in which the gas is in a steady-state condition. Only these situations will be considered here. While the apparatus indicated schematically in Fig. 2–1 is frequently employed to measure the *thermal conductivity* of gases, the analysis it requires is more complicated than we need. Hence we shall restrict our attention to another possible experimental arrangement, indicated in Fig. 2–2. In this arrangement, two parallel plates A_1 and A_2, each of equal area, are kept at fixed, different temperatures. They are separated by a distance D, the intervening region of uniform cross-sectional area being filled with the gas in question. (It is evident that a similar arrangement may be used to measure the thermal conductivity of any substance, not only of gases.) When a stationary-state condition of the gas is attained, the temperature at every position in the gas is constant as a function of time.

Provided that both the temperature difference $(T_2 - T_1)$ and the distance D between the plates are not too large, the experimental

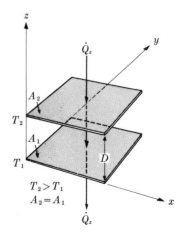

Fig. 2–2. Idealized heat conduction.

fact emerges that the temperature at each position depends linearly upon the distance of that position from one of the plates. In mathematical terms, one finds that

$$T(x, y, z) = T_1 + (T_2 - T_1) \frac{z}{D}. \tag{2-4}$$

The temperature at every point in a plane which is parallel to the plates A_1 and A_2 is the same. Only the distance of that plane from, say, A_1 need be specified to determine the temperature.

Associated with this arrangement is a flow of heat per unit of time in the z-direction, $\dot{Q}_z$, from the plate with the higher temperature to the one with the lower temperature. We need not elaborate on how this flow of heat is measured, but we emphasize that it can be accomplished in several ways. A determination of the rate of flow of heat, $\dot{Q}_z$, requires that the heat leaving the lower plate of Fig. 2–2 be measured in a known interval of time. By way of illustration, we can imagine that the lower plate is maintained at a fixed temperature by a heterogeneous mixture of solid and liquid phases of a pure substance. Then a measurement of the volume of either phase (or both) will yield a value for the amount of heat which the mixture has received since its preparation. Thus a sequence of such measurements made at known intervals of time enables $\dot{Q}_z$ to be computed. If the system is in a stationary state and Q_z calories flow in a time Δt seconds,

$$\dot{Q}_z = \frac{Q_z}{\Delta t} \text{ cal/sec.}$$

Note that no mathematical significance can be attached to a symbol such as dQ_z/dt, so we do not employ it for $\dot{Q}_z$.

Suppose, now, that two identical experimental arrangements are juxtaposed so that their corresponding plates are beside each other, as in Fig. 2–3.

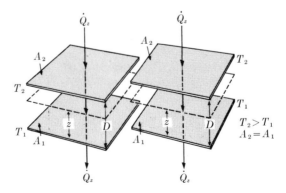

Fig. 2–3. Scaling relations in heat conduction.

Because of the identity of the temperatures as functions of position and time, Eq. (2–4) will also apply to the combination. However, the total flow of heat now will be the sum of the two heat flows, or double that of one in the present case. It follows by an extension of the argument that $\dot{Q}_z/A$, the flow of heat per unit time and per unit area, is independent of the area of the plates. We may, therefore, restrict our considerations to an arrangement in which a unit value of the cross-sectional area occurs.

In the experiment described, the total amount of heat which may be said to have entered the gas at A_2 must be eliminated at A_1. (Experimentally, this means that provisions must be made to avoid heat losses at the edge of the sample of gas. For this reason, the arrangement depicted in Fig. 2–1 is to be preferred over that of Fig. 2–2.) Otherwise, we should expect that the temperature at some positions would change with the passage of time. If the heat eliminated from A_1 is completely transferred to a second identical experimental arrangement, as in Fig. 2–4, it is observed that the lower temperature T_0 of the added apparatus must be fixed at a value given by

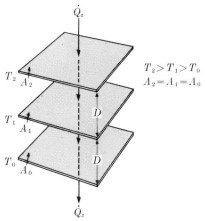

Fig. 2–4. Series arrangement in heat conduction.

$$T_0 = T_1 - (T_2 - T_1). \tag{2–5}$$

This follows from the observation that the *linear* dependence of temperature expressed in Eq. (2–4) must be extended to the new arrangement. In spite of the different temperatures involved, we note that

$$\frac{T_2 - T_1}{D} = \frac{T_2 - T_0}{2D} = \left(\frac{\partial T}{\partial z}\right)_{x,y}, \tag{2–6}$$

or that the *temperature gradient* $(\partial T/\partial z)_{x,y}$ is the same in the two arrangements. Thus, we can summarize the experimental facts so far discussed as follows:

$$\dot{Q}_z = A f\left[\left(\frac{\partial T}{\partial z}\right)_{x,y}\right], \tag{2–7}$$

where f is a function to be determined.

The function to be determined in Eq. (2–7) must satisfy an important restriction. Clearly, if we invert the apparatus in Fig. 2–2, but keep the various labels the same, the *magnitudes* of $\dot{Q}_z$ and $(\partial T/\partial z)_{x,y}$ will be unchanged. However, their *sign* will change, corresponding to an inversion of the *direction* of heat flow and temperature gradient. Hence we must require that f be such a function that

$$f(-x) = -f(x).$$

Moreover, we must obviously require that no heat flow (in the stationary state) occurs when there is no temperature gradient. Stated mathematically, we must have

$$f(0) = 0.$$

If we exploit these two requirements and assume that the function desired can be expanded in a power series of its argument, we must have only *odd* powers of that argument. Hence we can expect that Eq. (2–7) may be expressed as

$$\dot{q}_z \equiv \frac{\dot{Q}_z}{A} = -\kappa_1 \left(\frac{\partial T}{\partial z}\right)_{x,y} - \kappa_3 \left(\frac{\partial T}{\partial z}\right)_{x,y}^3 + \cdots, \qquad (2\text{–}8)$$

where each coefficient κ_i is independent of the temperature gradient, but may depend upon the gas and certain of its properties. For temperature gradients which are small (how small remains to be examined), the first term should be adequate, and we obtain

$$\dot{q}_z = -\kappa \left(\frac{\partial T}{\partial z}\right)_{x,y}, \qquad (2\text{–}9)$$

which is a simplified version of *Fourier's Law* of heat conduction. The quantity κ is termed the *coefficient of thermal conductivity*. (The sign is selected to assure that heat flows in the direction of decreasing temperature.)

It turns out that Eq. (2–9) is accurately satisfied in the limit that the distance between two parallel plates becomes indefinitely small. The heat flow then refers to the direction normal to the plates. A general temperature function will have gradients in directions other than the one we have indicated. For each direction, Eq. (2–9) is applicable, and expresses the heat flow per unit area and per unit time at a given *point* in the system in terms of the temperature gradient in that direction at that point. The coefficient of thermal conductivity in general depends upon the point in question and the direction. For gases, however, the latter variation is not manifested. In the present illustration, the quantities representing heat flows in the x- and y-directions, $\dot{q}_x$ and $\dot{q}_y$, are zero.

The mutually perpendicular directions of a cartesian coordinate system are adequate to describe the heat flow completely. Thus, in general, we may write

$$\dot{q}_x = -\kappa_x \left(\frac{\partial T}{\partial x}\right)_{y,z}, \qquad \dot{q}_y = -\kappa_y \left(\frac{\partial T}{\partial y}\right)_{z,x}, \qquad \dot{q}_z = -\kappa_z \left(\frac{\partial T}{\partial z}\right)_{x,y},$$

TABLE 2–1

VARIOUS COEFFICIENTS OF THERMAL CONDUCTIVITY
AND VISCOSITY OF GASES AT STP*

Gas	κ, 10^{-4} cal/cm·sec·°C	η, 10^{-4} poise	W, gm/gm-mole
He	3.52	1.89	4.0
Ne	1.09	2.98	20.2
Ar	0.40	2.10	39.9
Kr	0.21	2.33	83.8
Xe	0.12	2.11	131.3
H_2	4.16	0.85	2.0
D_2	3.08	1.18	4.0
CO	0.56	1.67	28.0
N_2	0.58	1.67	28.0
NO	0.56	1.79	30.0
O_2	0.59	1.93	32.0
Cl_2	0.18	1.22	70.9
C_2H_4	0.41	.96	28.0

* From data in S. Chapman and T. G. Cowling, *Mathematical Theory of Nonuniform Gases*, pp. 229, 241. New York: Cambridge University Press (1950). Also J. R. Partington, *Advanced Treatise on Physical Chemistry*, Vol. I, pp. 858–861. London: Longmans, Green and Company (1949).

where we have allowed for the possibility that the coefficient of thermal conductivity may vary with direction. When the latter is *isotropic*, the previous equations may be rendered into a simple *vector equation:*

$$\dot{\mathbf{q}} = -\kappa \nabla T,$$

the components of $\dot{\mathbf{q}}$ and ∇T being those indicated above. When the coefficient of thermal conductivity is not isotropic, a more complicated equation, which we avoid, must be written.

Some values of the coefficients of thermal conductivity for gases are given in Table 2–1. There does not appear to be any simple dependence of these values upon the nature of the gas. Thus the molecular weight is not a unique correlant; helium and hydrogen have almost the same values of the coefficients in spite of a difference by a factor of two in their molecular weights. Nevertheless, the qualitative trends with molecular weight are noteworthy, if not exact. Molecules with large molecular weight seem to exhibit smaller values of thermal conductivity coefficients than do those with smaller molecular weights. The variation with temperature of the

TABLE 2–2

RELATIVE THERMAL CONDUCTIVITIES OF VARIOUS GASES
AT DIFFERENT TEMPERATURES*

Gas	Temperature, °K	κ/κ (273°K)
H_2	273	1.00
	195	.77
	82	.34
	21	.08
He	273	1.00
	82	0.44
	21	0.16
CO	273	1.00
	195	.73
	82	.30

* Eucken, *Phys. Z.*, **12**, 1101 (1911); **14**, 324 (1913).

coefficients of thermal conductivity is indicated in Table 2–2. Again, no simple relation seems apparent, although the coefficients increase in value as the temperature is increased, the relative increase being somewhat less than the relative increase in absolute temperature. The effect of pressure upon the thermal conductivity coefficients is slight at ordinary values of the pressure, being then almost independent of the pressure.

The latter behavior is somewhat surprising, but it is not fulfilled at extremely low and high pressures. As the pressure becomes smaller and smaller, the amount of gas in any finite region approaches zero. In the limit of no gas at all, we can anticipate no thermal conductivity. The onset of this decrease, however, occurs at extremely low pressures, the value of which depends upon the size of the thermal conductivity apparatus. We shall later see reasons for this behavior. At pressures much higher than atmospheric, the thermal conductivity of gases increases. We can rationalize this behavior from the intimate relation prevailing between gases and liquids. At sufficiently high pressures, the compressed gas is indistinguishable from the liquid, and its properties should approach those of the liquid.

The important thing to keep in mind in regard to the gaseous thermal conductivity coefficients under ordinary conditions is their small value when compared with those of liquids and solids. Some typical values of the latter are given in Table 2–3. A factor of about ten is to be noted between the liquid values and those of Table 2–1.

TABLE 2–3

COEFFICIENTS OF THERMAL CONDUCTIVITY OF
VARIOUS SOLIDS AND LIQUIDS AT 15°C*

Substance	κ, 10^{-4} cal/cm·sec·°C
Acetic Acid	4.7
Ethyl Alcohol	4.2
Water	14.4
Chloroform	2.9
Benzene	3.3
Cork	1.3
Glass	20
Marble	71
Aluminum	5,140
Copper	10,000
Lead	830

* Data from *Handbook of Chemistry and Physics.*
Cleveland: Chemical Rubber Publishing Company.

3. MASS TRANSPORT IN GASES

The seeming rapidity with which gases mix, or diffuse through one another, is an obvious fact emerging from observations made upon odoriferous substances like hydrogen sulfide and ammonia. However, the same sort of mixing process occurs in liquids and solids, although much less rapidly than in gases. To provide a quantitative distinction between these two sorts of behavior, we must make an analysis of the diffusive process.

As in the case of thermal conductivity, we contemplate a simplified version of an experiment designed to measure the rate of diffusion of gases. The arrangement in Fig. 2–2 is modified as follows. The plates A_1 and A_2 are replaced by membranes which are permeable to the diffusing gases. They serve to restrain the gas in the intervening region and prevent its mechanical motion. On the exterior side of each membrane (opposite to the confined region), a gas of fixed, specified composition is continually supplied. Thus the gaseous composition on the exterior may be maintained constant in time even though passage of each constituent is possible through the membrane. By measuring the amount of each constituent leaving the membrane region and comparing it with the amount entering, the rate of diffusion of each constituent may be determined. A schematic diagram of the experimental apparatus is shown in Fig. 2–5.

When a stationary condition is attained, a linear variation in the concentration of each constituent is observed in the diffusing region. This

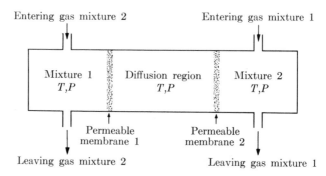

Fig. 2–5. Steady-state diffusion arrangement.

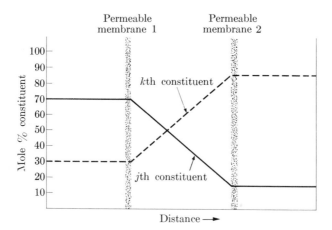

Fig. 2–6. Diagram of composition variation in diffusion.

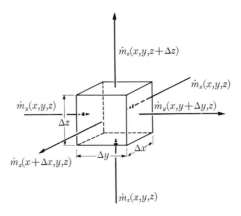

Fig. 2–7. Diffusion through small volume element.

behavior is indicated in Fig. 2–6, for a binary gas mixture. For chemically unreactive gases at ordinary temperatures and pressures, the temperature and pressure have uniform values throughout the region. With an application of the "scaling" arguments used previously for the thermal conductivity experiment, we can obtain an equation for the diffusion rate of any one of the substances. For the kth substance, we can obtain (note the sign convention)

$$\frac{1}{A}\, \dot{m}_k = -D_k \left(\frac{\partial C_k}{\partial z} \right)_{x,y}, \qquad (2\text{--}10)$$

where A is the cross-sectional area, expressed in cm^2, through which the kth substance is diffusing at the rate of $\dot{m}_k$ gm/sec, and C_k is the concentration at some point in the diffusing region, expressed in gm/cm^3. (Any consistent set of units will do.) Clearly, the concentration gradient in the present case is

$$\left(\frac{\partial C_k}{\partial z} \right)_{x,y} = \frac{C_k(2) - C_k(1)}{D}.$$

The quantity D_k is termed the *diffusion coefficient* or the *diffusivity* of the kth substance. An equation of the form of Eq. (2–10) is available for each substance and is a simplified version of *Fick's First Law* of diffusion.

While we restrict our consideration to stationary processes, it may be indicated how Fick's Law can be adapted to those which are nonstationary. In terms of the diagram in Fig. 2–7, the diffusive flow may be different for opposite faces of an arbitrarily small cubical element of volume. Each such difference results in a change in the total amount of the substance in the indicated volume. Clearly, this total change in *concentration* can be expressed as

$$\frac{\partial}{\partial t} C_k(x, y, z, t) \doteq \left\{ \frac{\dot{m}_{k,x}(x + \Delta x, y, z) - \dot{m}_{k,x}(x, y, z)}{\Delta x\, \Delta y\, \Delta z} \right\}$$
$$+ \left\{ \frac{\dot{m}_{k,y}(x, y + \Delta y, z) - \dot{m}_{k,y}(x, y, z)}{\Delta x\, \Delta y\, \Delta z} \right\}$$
$$+ \left\{ \frac{\dot{m}_{k,z}(x, y, z + \Delta z) - \dot{m}_{k,z}(x, y, z)}{\Delta x\, \Delta y\, \Delta z} \right\}.$$

Assuming that D_k is constant and independent of direction, and substituting in Eq. (2–10), we obtain in the limit as $\Delta x \to 0$, $\Delta y \to 0$, $\Delta z \to 0$,

$$\frac{\partial C_k}{\partial t} = -D_k \left\{ \frac{\partial^2 C_k}{\partial x^2} + \frac{\partial^2 C_k}{\partial y^2} + \frac{\partial^2 C_k}{\partial z^2} \right\},$$

where the definition of a partial derivative has been invoked. (See, for example, p. 16.) In this latter form, *Fick's Second Law* is expressible entirely in terms of a *partial differential equation* in the concentration, regarded as a function of position and time.

TABLE 2–4

CERTAIN BINARY DIFFUSION COEFFICIENTS OF GASES AT STP*

Pair	D_{12}, cm²/sec
ortho H_2—para H_2	1.28
H_2—D_2	1.13
H_2—N_2	0.67
H_2—O_2	0.70
CO—N_2	0.19
CO—C_2H_4	0.12
CO_2—N_2O	0.10

* From S. Chapman and T. G. Cowling, *Mathematical Theory of Nonuniform Gases,* p. 252. New York: Cambridge University Press (1950).

In the simple case we are considering, there is an important restriction upon the diffusion coefficients of the two substances. Since the pressure and temperature are constant, and independent of position in the diffusing region, there must be a relation between the concentration gradients of the two substances. At very small pressures, the gases may be treated as ideal gases with good approximation. Under such conditions, it follows that the molar *concentration* of the mixture (see p. 18) must also be constant throughout the region. But then it follows that

$$\frac{1}{W_j}\left(\frac{\partial C_j}{\partial z}\right)_{x,y} + \frac{1}{W_k}\left(\frac{\partial C_k}{\partial z}\right)_{x,y} = 0.$$

In order to maintain constant pressure in the regions exterior to the diffusing region, there must likewise be constancy in the total number of gram-moles (under the stated conditions). Hence it follows that

$$\frac{1}{W_j}\,\dot{m}_j + \frac{1}{W_k}\,\dot{m}_k = 0.$$

These two restrictions, when combined with Eq. (2–10) and an analogous one for the jth substance, lead to the conclusion that

$$D_j = D_k \equiv D_{jk}, \tag{2–11}$$

or that the *binary* diffusion constants must be the same for both substances. This relation is exact only under conditions where the gases behave like ideal gases, but it is closely approximated by real gases under ordinary

TABLE 2–5

BINARY DIFFUSION COEFFICIENTS OF CERTAIN
LIQUIDS INTO PURE WATER*

Substance	Temperature	D_{12}, cm^2/day
1.0M Acetic acid	12°C	0.74
1.0M Ammonia	15°C	1.54
1.0M Glycerine	10°C	0.34
1.0M KBr	20°C	1.13
1.0M NaCl	15°C	0.94

* Data from *Handbook of Chemistry and Physics.*
Cleveland: Chemical Rubber Publishing Co.

conditions of temperature and pressure. In any case, it is clear that the "diffusion coefficient of a substance" represents a property which is not intrinsic to it, but refers implicitly to the medium in which diffusion occurs.

In Table 2–4 are given some binary diffusion coefficients at conditions of standard temperature and pressure. No precise correlation with the molecular weight is apparent, but species of low molecular weight generally exhibit larger diffusivities than those with high molecular weights. In general, a slight dependence of the diffusion coefficient upon the composition of the binary mixture is observed. Of greater import is the observation that at low densities the diffusion coefficients of gases vary inversely as the density. Their temperature variation is usually small.

For comparison, diffusion coefficients of liquids are given in Table 2–5. Note that the values are markedly smaller than those of Table 2–4, by an apparent factor of about 10^4.

4. VISCOUS BEHAVIOR OF GASES

It is doubtful that any single property can be found which will provide a means for clearly distinguishing between gases and liquids. The illustrations we have considered reduce any such distinction to a matter of *degree.* This is not unexpected, considering the intimate relation that exists between these two states of matter (i.e., critical phenomenon). However, there is a property which enables us to distinguish clearly between fluids and solids. It is the *static resistance* offered by substances to a *shear stress:* fluids offer no static resistance to such a stress, while solids do. This may be made clear by means of Fig. 2–8. A small amount of material, either solid or fluid, is confined to the shape of a rectangular parallelepiped by a completely flexible membrane. When a small *couple* of forces is applied

Solid

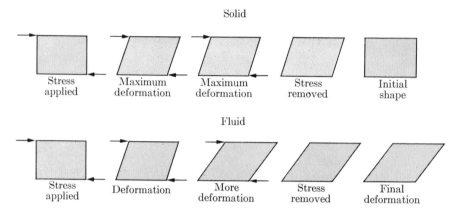

| Stress applied | Maximum deformation | Maximum deformation | Stress removed | Initial shape |

Fluid

| Stress applied | Deformation | More deformation | Stress removed | Final deformation |

Fig. 2–8. Schematic behavior of solid and fluid under shear stress.

to opposite faces of the parallelepiped, it may be expected to deform. The accompanying stress is termed a *shear*. When the stress is reduced to zero, the solid parallelepiped will assume its original shape, while the fluid one will not. This behavior will be observed *no matter how small the stress is.* Furthermore, while solids will exhibit a limiting deformation depending upon the magnitude of the stress, liquids continue to deform indefinitely for any nonzero stress. The rate at which such deformation occurs is determined by the *viscous* behavior of the fluid, to which we now turn our attention.

Fig. 2–9. Schematics of viscous flow.

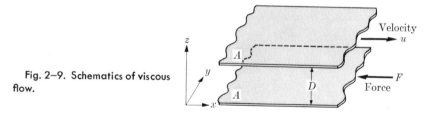

For simplicity, we consider a gas confined to a region bounded by two extended parallel plates. This arrangement is indicated schematically in Fig. 2–9. (For conceptual purposes the plates are designed to be "large" in order to render negligible any edge effects upon the system. In practical terms, other forms of the apparatus are employed. This requires a somewhat more complicated analysis than the one given here.) Due to an external force, the upper plate may be imagined as moving with respect to the lower one, which may be regarded as stationary. For a fixed velocity of the upper plate, it is found that a force parallel to the velocity and opposite in direction must be applied to the lower plate in order that it remain stationary. This force is opposed to one said to arise from the *viscous drag* of the gas. If we designate the latter as F, it is evident that for a given gas

$$F = F(u, D, A),$$

where u is the velocity of the upper plate, D the distance between them, and A their individual areas. By scaling the apparatus in terms of area, as we have done previously, we infer that the viscous force must be proportional to the area of the plate:

$$\mathfrak{F} = \frac{F}{A} = \mathfrak{F}(u, D).$$

Now, we imagine that the macroscopic velocity of the gas is a function only of the distance from one of the plates. The situation we are describing corresponds to a *laminar flow* of the gas. We can regard the viscous force as due to a fictitious plate moving with such a layer. Then, writing

$$u_z = u(z),$$

we may see that

$$\mathfrak{F} = \mathfrak{F}(u_D, D) = \mathfrak{F}(u_z, z)$$

is a quantity *independent of z*. Hence, the viscous force has a value determined entirely by the properties of the gas flowing in the immediate vicinity of the stationary plate.

Since the velocity of the gas in the immediate vicinity of the stationary plate is zero, for reasons of continuity, it is evident that the viscous force cannot depend explicitly upon the velocity of the gas immediately near the plate. Otherwise, changes in u_D and D would result in no changes in the viscous force. This behavior contradicts the facts. Upon what may the viscous force depend? Although $u(0)$ vanishes, its gradient need not. Thus, we may suppose that

$$\mathfrak{F} = \mathfrak{F}\left\{\left(\frac{\partial u}{\partial z}\right)_{x,y}\right\}.$$

With a repetition of the arguments employed for thermal conductivity and diffusion, we obtain

$$\mathfrak{F} = -\eta\left(\frac{\partial u}{\partial z}\right)_{x,y}, \tag{2–12}$$

an expression originally obtained by Newton. The quantity η is called the coefficient of viscosity. It can be expressed in terms of units of dynes·sec/cm^2, such a quantity being referred to as a *poise*.

Of the three gaseous transport properties we have mentioned, perhaps the most widely investigated one is viscosity. Some of the values are given in Table 2–1. No significant trends with molecular weight are to be noted.

TABLE 2–6

VISCOSITY COEFFICIENTS FOR CERTAIN
LIQUIDS AT 20°C*

Substance	η, 10^{-2} poise
Acetic acid	1.30
Ethyl alcohol	1.20
Glycerine	1490
Chloroform	0.58
Benzene	0.65
Water	1.00
Water at 40°C	0.65
Water at 60°C	0.47
Water at 80°C	0.36
Mercury	1.55

* Data from *Handbook of Chemistry and Physics*. Cleveland: Chemical Rubber Publishing Co.

In general, viscosity coefficients of gases increase with increasing temperature. Experimental data yield no simple temperature function, but suggest a variation less than proportionality to the absolute temperature. Most remarkable is the pressure dependence of viscosity. Except for extremely small or large values of the pressure the viscosity coefficient is insensitive to changes in pressure. This behavior is similar to that already noted for the coefficients of thermal conductivity. The remarks made there pertain here as well.

For comparison, Table 2–6 lists the viscosity coefficients of a number of liquids. Liquid values are considerably larger, by about a factor of 10^2. Moreover, viscosity coefficients of liquids usually *decrease* relatively markedly with increasing temperature.

5. CORRELATIONS AMONG TRANSPORT PROPERTIES

We have looked for but have not succeeded in finding any simple correlations of the various transport properties of gases with their molecular weight, which correlation proved to be so successful for the equation of state. Yet, that there should be some sort of correlation appears reasonable. One obvious possibility for our failure is suggested by the behavior of binary diffusion coefficients. Since these quantities depend upon the pair of gases involved, it is evident that other elementary properties *in*

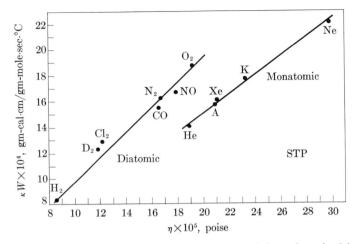

Fig. 2–10. Correlation between gaseous viscosity and thermal conductivity.

addition to the molecular weight may be involved. To disclose these elementary properties is, in fact, the object of the theoretical analysis to be undertaken presently.

For the present, however, we wish to draw attention to certain similarities in the transport properties from an experimental viewpoint. In Fig. 2–10 we have plotted the product of the molecular weight and the coefficient of thermal conductivity for several gases against the corresponding values of the viscosity coefficient. Although not perfect, a good correlation of these two quantities is evident. However, it is also evident that they correlate well only if the gases are separated into monatomic, diatomic, etc. A close examination of the graphs will disclose that there is no regularity as regards molecular weight alone. Because there is a distinction to be noted between the correlations of monatomic and diatomic gases, we can anticipate the involvement of some property in the correlation which depends upon the *number of atoms* in the molecules.

A correlation of diffusivities with viscosity coefficients entails some difficulty, since the former involves more than a single substance. What we want are the coefficients of *self-diffusion*, and these are impossible to measure directly, although with an appropriate theory they can be computed from the measured binary diffusion coefficients. However, for gases which do not differ in molecular weight, we may take a *geometric mean* of the viscosity coefficients of the two gases to correlate with the binary diffusion coefficient. Such a value is somewhat arbitrary but appears to work, as indicated in Fig. 2–11. Again, note the absence of any regularity with reference to the molecular weights alone. There is no apparent correlation with the number of atoms, contrary to what we found in connection with the correlation between thermal conductivity and viscosity.

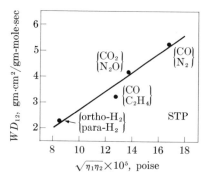

Fig. 2–11. Correlation between gaseous viscosity and diffusion.

The simple correlations existing between the gaseous transport properties of thermal conductivity, diffusivity, and viscosity suggest a nontrivial similarity between these processes. Wherein does it lie? In each of these processes there is a transport of something: heat, matter, and force, respectively. We can easily imagine systems in which either heat or force is transported, without an analogous transport of matter. We need only think of a solid which conducts heat by virtue of a temperature gradient. Likewise, a solid subjected to shear is effectively transferring force, although in a manner by no means similar to that involved in a viscous fluid. In fact, since no motion of the solid need be involved, $(\partial u/\partial z)_{x,y}$ is zero for solids, and the viscosity coefficient which would be given by Eq. (2–12) is indefinitely large (i.e., infinite). (This could have been anticipated, of course, from the discussion given previously, which led to a distinction between solids and fluids.) In the case of solids, therefore, no correlation exists between the transport of heat and of force. Likewise, no correlation will be found between diffusivity in solids and thermal conductivity, although we shall not elaborate upon this. Hence the correlation we have observed to exist in gases is striking.

The fact that the gaseous transport properties are correlated with one another suggests strongly that they have a common origin. Recognizing that diffusion obviously represents a transport of matter through the gaseous system, we can anticipate that the phenomena of thermal conductivity and viscosity in gases likewise involve a common transport of matter. (Hence, they are termed transport properties.) In the succeeding theoretical treatment of gases, the common features of the transport properties described in this chapter will be elaborated.

6. SUMMARY

The transport properties of nonuniform gases, i.e., thermal conductivity, diffusivity, and viscosity, have been discussed. Of particular interest has been a comparison of these properties for gases and liquids. We have established that the gaseous transport properties correlate with one another and involve the molecular weight of the gas.

EXERCISES

1. An apparatus consists of two concentric circular cylinders with the diameter of the inner one being 1 meter and with an annular spacing between the cylinders of 1 mm. The height of the annulus is 10.0 cm. The annulus is filled with water at 20°C and the inner cylinder is rotated about its axis at a fixed speed of 10.0 rpm. Estimate the tangential force required to maintain the outer cylinder stationary.
   Answer: 16.3 gf.

2. Assuming that a material can be found which is perfectly permeable only to hydrogen, imagine an apparatus constructed as follows. A tube 1 meter long having a cross-sectional area of 10.0 cm^2 is filled with nitrogen at a pressure of approximately $\frac{1}{2}$ atm and at 0°C. The ends are then sealed with the hydrogen-permeable material. One end is put in contact with a source of hydrogen at STP, while the other end is in contact with a vacuum. Ultimately, a steady-state condition is attained in which the gases within the tube are at STP. Estimate the flow rate of hydrogen through the tube.
   Answer: 0.0215 gm/hr.

3. Two parallel plates, as in Fig. 2–2, are each of 100.0 cm^2 area and are spaced 1.00 cm apart. One plate is kept at 10.0°C by some means, the other plate at 0.0°C by being in thermal contact with a mixture of ice and water. The region between the plates is filled with air at approximately atmospheric pressure. (a) Given that the latent heat of fusion of ice is 79.7 cal/gm, estimate the rate of melting of ice in the freezing mixture (assuming no other sources of heat). (b) Taking the density of liquid water as 1.000 gm/ml and that of ice as 0.917 gm/ml, estimate the rate of volume change.
   Answers: (a) 0.0441 gm/min; (b) −0.0040 ml/min.

4. To obtain a correlation between a transport property and an equilibrium property, plot $(\eta/W^{1/2})$ versus the molal volume at the normal boiling point Tables 1–5 and 2–1. (Except for hydrogen and helium, a correlation will be suggested. $\eta/W^{1/2}$ decreases with increasing $\overline{V}_b$.) Try also a correlation with van der Waals' b for the substance.

5. Starting with Fick's Second Law for the diffusion in one dimension, confirm that the steady state corresponds to linear variations of concentration with distance.

6. Consider three equally spaced thin parallel plates as in Fig. 2–4, each made of an excellent thermal conductor such as a metal. Let the region between one pair of plates be filled with water while the region between the other pair is filled with hydrogen gas. Disregarding the temperature variation of thermal conductivity, obtain an expression for the temperature of the intermediate plate T_i in terms of the temperature of the outside plates, T_W and T_{H_2} respectively.
   Answer: $T_i = 0.776\,T_W + 0.224\,T_{H_2}$.

7. Estimate the molecular flow rate which must be present in order to maintain a concentration difference in one centimeter of a CO-N$_2$ mixture of 10^{-6} gm-mole/liter.
   Answer: 1.15×10^{13} molecules/cm^2 · sec.

3 · KINETIC-MOLECULAR THEORY OF IDEAL GASES

1. MOLECULAR FEATURES OF AN IDEAL GAS

The gaseous physical properties we have selected for description have required no essential reference to be made to their molecular constitution. Nevertheless, we have not shut our minds to just such a possibility. Indeed, we have found it useful to exploit the molecular constitution of gases in order to simplify the expression of their equations of state. But such exploitation has merely entailed dealing with amounts of each gas which are measured in units of its molecular weight. The latter unit appears to be useful also in correlating certain of the transport properties of gases with each other. However, the molecular weight of a gas can be viewed as a characteristic quantity of that gas, the value of which can be determined *without any explicit reference to molecules*. (For gases at very small pressures, we need to use Eq. (1–13), which can be regarded as an *empirical* relation defining the molecular weight of each gas.)

From Eq. (1–13) we obtain the expression

$$W = R\left(\frac{mT}{PV}\right),$$

where the quantity in parentheses is determined entirely from measured values of the pertinent properties. The value of R is determined only if the molecular weight of some one gas is known. Consequently, only *relative* molecular weights are determinable, in principle, from measurements. That is,

$$\frac{W_1}{W_2} = \frac{m_1 T_1/P_1 V_1}{m_2 T_2/P_2 V_2},$$

where 1, 2 refer to any two gases, is all that can be determined in terms of the indicated measured properties of the gases.

It is not our intention to exaggerate this viewpoint. On the contrary, the fact that we can find a characteristic quantity which is independent of the state of the gas, either uniform or nonuniform, is of the greatest importance. In terms of the properties we have considered, the appearance of the molecular weight in expressions involving the apparently *static properties* and those involving the *transport properties* cannot fail to suggest

60

the existence of an intrinsic relation between these obviously diverse properties of gases.

We have already anticipated that thermal conductivity, viscosity, and diffusion in gases involve the common transport of matter. If this is correct, the presence of the molecular weight in the correlations we have exhibited prompts the suggestion that the molecular weight is related to that which is transported. The presence of the molecular weight in the equation of state of a gas (a relation among apparently static properties) further suggests that the properties of pressure and temperature are not as "static" as they appear. (The volume is obviously excluded, since it is actually determined by the container and not by the gas.) These suggestions can be made more precise in terms of a kinetic-molecular theory of gases, which we shall elaborate. However, the aspect of *molecular constitution* emerges with impeccable clarity from the relations among the combining weights of chemical substances, as inferred by Dalton. Only then is it clear as to what the molecular weight relates: the mass of the individual molecules of each substance. The kinetic aspect of the theory can only emerge from the properties we have described.

In order to formulate a theory of gases which incorporates (1) the hypothesis of molecular constitution of matter, and (2) the hypothesis of kinetic behavior of the molecules, we must turn to the observed behavior of gases for guidance. Since real gases exhibit individualities which cannot be suppressed, even within the framework of a Corresponding States Relation, it is evident that a general theory of gases must be a complicated affair if it is to deal with each gas in an appropriate manner. However, the ideal gas has an essential simplicity about it, requiring only the values of the molecular weight to give distinction to those gases which satisfy an identical equation of state. For such gases we can anticipate a theory which is far simpler. However, even for ideal gases we can anticipate that the transport properties will not be adequately accounted for. (Below certain small values of the pressure, the coefficients of thermal conductivity and viscosity tend to decrease in value, presumably vanishing as the pressure tends toward zero. The diffusivities become extremely large at vanishingly low pressures.) Nevertheless, such a theory can be useful because of its simplicity; with further guidance from the observed behavior of gases, we shall see how it can be later augmented to deal with real gases at low pressures.

There are three properties of ideal gases which can furnish an insight into the kinetic-molecular theory we wish to construct. These are the following:

1. *Ideal gases have enormously large diffusivities.* This fact is an extrapolation of the behavior of real gases at small pressures. It suggests two things:

(a) the molecular constituents of an ideal gas are capable of extremely rapid motion; and (b) the molecules are so small as to offer no appreciable impediment to the diffusive flow. In turn, there appears to be no deterrent to the motion of the molecules of an ideal gas within the bulk of the gas.

2. *The uniform ideal gas is isotropic.* There is no directional dependence for the properties of an ideal gas. This behavior suggests that whatever molecular motion exists is of such a nature that the motions assume no preferred direction. Loosely stated, the directional motion of molecules is entirely random for uniform ideal gases. Individual molecules which may be moving in a stipulated direction must correlate with others moving in the opposite sense.

3. *Uniform ideal gases are in a stationary state.* This trivial observation has a nontrivial implication for molecular motions. The entire motion of the molecules of an ideal gas is unchanging with the passage of time, unless something external is done to alter that motion. From the viewpoint of individual molecules, any change in the motion of one must be correlated with a compensatory change in some other molecule, or molecules.

These intuitive ideas can be expressed more precisely in terms of a kinetic-molecular *model* of an ideal gas. Such a model comprises the *physical* assumptions of the theory. They are:

1. Each ideal gas consists of a collection of molecules which have no spatial extension whatever; each molecule is a *mass-point*. The mass of each molecule is proportional to the molecular weight of the (pure) ideal gas of which it is a constituent.

2. Each molecule moves unimpeded through the bulk of the ideal gas. Its motion is constrained only by macroscopic objects with which the ideal gas is in contact.

3. In each region of the ideal gas, at any instant of time, the likelihood of finding some molecule moving in some specified direction is the same as for any other direction.

4. For all times, the likelihood of finding some molecule with a specified speed (or range of speeds) is always the same.

5. The motion of molecules satisfies Newton's Laws of Motion.

The first four statements can be seen to correspond to the intuitive notions we have discussed. The fifth one provides the theoretical machinery, so to speak, with which to construct the theory—lacking it, we have no prescription with which to exploit the previous assumptions. However, this last assumption cannot be regarded as being explicitly related to the theory of gases. It has far wider applicability. In fact, by its introduction we are asserting that the theory we propose to construct must be consistent with the general mechanical behavior of systems, gaseous or not. For this reason, a review of the mechanics of particles seems worth while.

2. MECHANICS OF PARTICLES

Consider a particle having a mass m, and suppose that its motion is confined to a straight line which we may identify as the x-axis of a cartesian coordinate system. Its location is completely specified by the value of the x-coordinate of its center of mass. If it is moving, its velocity along the axis at each instant of time t is

$$v_x(t) \equiv \frac{dx(t)}{dt} \equiv \dot{x}(t), \qquad (3\text{-}1)$$

where $x(t)$ is the location of the particle at time t. If, due to an external force, the velocity of the particle alters with time, we attribute an acceleration

$$a_x(t) \equiv \frac{dv_x(t)}{dt} \equiv \frac{d^2x(t)}{dt^2} \equiv \ddot{x}(t) \qquad (3\text{-}2)$$

to the particle at each instant of time. It can be seen that, apart from any additional relations existing between the quantities which have been introduced, we have

$$x(t_2) - x(t_1) = \int_{t_1}^{t_2} dt\, v_x(t),$$

and

$$v_x(t_2) - v_x(t_1) = \int_{t_1}^{t_2} dt\, a_x(t).$$

Consequently, substitution of the last equation into the previous one yields

$$x(t_2) - x(t_1) = \int_{t_1}^{t_2} dt \left[v_x(t_1) + \int_{t_1}^{t} d\tau\, a_x(\tau) \right]$$

$$= (t_2 - t_1)v_x(t_1) + \int_{t_1}^{t_2} dt \int_{t_1}^{t} d\tau\, a_x(\tau).$$

The displacement of the particle, $x(t_2) - x(t_1)$, is thus determined if its initial velocity $v_x(t_1)$ is known and its acceleration $a_x(\tau)$ is known for all values of the time τ in the interval (t_2, t_1). When the acceleration has a constant value g, independent of the time,

$$x(t_2) - x(t_1) = (t_2 - t_2)v_x(t_1) + \tfrac{1}{2}g(t_2 - t_1)^2,$$

a well-known equation for the fall of objects in the gravitational field of the earth.

The importance of Newton's Laws of Motion is that they provide a relationship between the mass and the acceleration of a particle and the force acting upon it. They may be summarized in the equation

$$f_x(t) = ma_x(t),\qquad(3\text{--}3)$$

where $f_x(t)$ is the force acting upon the particle in the x-direction at time t. By means of this equation, the displacement experienced by a particle is related to its initial velocity and the subsequent forces acting upon it. In a reciprocal manner, Eq. (3–3) permits the *calculation* of the force acting upon a particle from the measured values of its mass and its acceleration at any instant, the latter being computed from a knowledge of the measured displacement as a function of time, $x(t)$.

Equation (3–3) is an equation of *classical mechanics*. From our present knowledge of the detailed behavior of microscopic systems, a new mechanics, *quantum mechanics*, must be used to describe their behavior. Nevertheless, Eq. (3–3) has its counterpart in quantum mechanics, and so its use for molecular systems is not completely unjustified. Except for particles of extremely small mass and small velocities, the error introduced by the use of classical mechanics is relatively small and negligible.

We may rewrite Eq. (3–3) in a form which will have subsequent utility. Making use of Eq. (3–2) and the definition of *momentum*,

$$p_x(t) \equiv mv_x(t),$$

we obtain

$$f_x(t) = \frac{dp_x(t)}{dt}.\qquad(3\text{--}4)$$

If we integrate this equation, we obtain

$$p_x(t_2) - p_x(t_1) = \int_{t_1}^{t_2} dt\, f_x(t),\qquad(3\text{--}5)$$

or that the change in momentum experienced by a particle is equal to the time-integral of the force acting upon it. The latter is called the *impulse* acting upon the particle. In the absence of any force acting upon a particle, its momentum is constant for all times. One says that, under these conditions, the momentum of the particle is *conserved*.

Under identical conditions of *isolation*, the *kinetic energy* of a particle,

$$T(t) \equiv \tfrac{1}{2}m[v_x(t)]^2 = \frac{[p_x(t)]^2}{2m},\qquad(3\text{--}6)$$

is also conserved. To see this, notice that

$$T(t_2) - T(t_1) = \int_{t_1}^{t_2} dt\,\frac{dT_x(t)}{dt} = m\int_{t_1}^{t_2} dt\, v_x(t)\,\frac{dv_x(t)}{dt},\qquad(3\text{--}7)$$

where use has been made of the definition of kinetic energy. With the aid of Eqs. (3–1)–(3–3), we obtain

$$T(t_2) - T(t_1) = \int_{t_1}^{t_2} dt\, f_x(t)\, \frac{dx(t)}{dt}$$

$$= \int_{x(t_1)}^{x(t_2)} dx\, f_x[t(x)], \qquad (3\text{–}8)$$

where we have changed to the position of the particle as a variable of integration. [This point is clarified in the discussion following Eq. (3–10).] In the absence of any applied force, the integral vanishes and the kinetic energy is conserved, as asserted. The integral on the right side of Eq. (3–8) is referred to as the *work* done upon the particle. It is possible for the force acting upon a particle to be different from zero for most of the time of its action and yet have no work done by the force. (A trivial example is one in which the force is fixed in magnitude, but changes sign in adjacent, equal intervals of displacement of the particle.)

A special but important class of situations occurs for which the force is the x-derivative of some function. That is, for these situations

$$f_x(x) = -\frac{dV(x)}{dx}, \qquad (3\text{–}9)$$

where $V(x)$ does not depend *explicitly* upon the time; the precise form of $V(x)$ varies from one system to another and from one situation to another. When Eq. (3–9) holds, the force is said to be *derivable from a potential* and $V(x)$ is termed the *potential energy function* for the system (or particle). With Eq. (3–9) we can evaluate the integral of Eq. (3–8) and obtain

$$T(t_2) - T(t_1) = -[V[x(t_2)] - V[x(t_1)]],$$

or

$$T(t_2) + V[x(t_2)] = T(t_1) + V[x(t_1)]. \qquad (3\text{–}10)$$

The quantity in Eq. (3–10) is called the *total energy* (or simply the energy) of the particle, and is a quantity which is conserved for all systems for which the force is derivable from a potential. Hence, such forces are referred to as *conservative forces*. [We can easily verify that if Eq. (3–10) is valid for all values of t_2, then Eq. (3–9) must also hold.]

The significance of conservative forces, defined by Eq. (3–9) lies in the fact that they are independent of the actual motion of the particle. In general, the motion of a particle can be described by the function $x(t)$. This motion may be said to have been "caused" by $f_x(t)$. Because position and time are correlated, we have a function $t(x)$ which is the time it takes for the particle to reach x and which *depends upon the actual motion exhibited by the particle*. In the presence of arbitrary forces, $f_x(t)$, the function $t(x)$ may be varied arbitrarily. It is such a force which may be employed in Eq. (3–8), and is designated as $f_x[t(x)]$. By contrast, $f_x(x)$ defined by Eq. (3–9) is independent of the actual motion of the particle, in the sense that the force depends only upon where the particle is, and not, as in $f_x[t(x)]$, upon how long it takes to get there.

The results of the present section may be extended in two ways. The first of these involves more than a single particle; the second, more than a single direction of motion. We shall take first things first.

Consider two particles a and b which are constrained, as before, to motion along the x-axis. The previous equations apply to each particle. In particular, we will suppose that the two particles may have different masses and have only a mutual conservative force acting upon them which depends only upon the distance between them. That is, the potential energy function

$$V = V(x_b - x_a)$$

will yield the conservative forces acting upon the two particles. Such potentials are called *central force potentials*. Explicitly, the resulting force acting upon particle a is

$$f_{x_a} = -\frac{\partial V(x_b - x_a)}{\partial x_a} = V'(x_b - x_a),$$

where $V'(y)$ is the total derivative dV/dy, and the resulting force acting upon particle b is

$$f_{x_b} = -\frac{\partial V(x_b - x_a)}{\partial x_b} = -V'(x_b - x_a).$$

Clearly, for all distances between the particles,

$$f_{x_b} = -f_{x_a}. \tag{3–11}$$

The mutual forces acting upon two particles are equal in magnitude but opposite in sense.

The foregoing relation, the result of the central forces acting between the particles, has a consequence of some importance. To obtain this, we employ Eqs. (3–2) and (3–3). We have

$$m_a \ddot{x}_a = f_{x_a} = -f_{x_b} = -m_b \ddot{x}_b. \tag{3–12}$$

Hence

$$\frac{d^2}{dt^2}(m_a x_a + m_b x_b) = 0. \tag{3–13}$$

This equation has a form which is identical to that of a free particle (i.e., no force acting upon it) of mass

$$m_{ab} = m_a + m_b \tag{3–14a}$$

located at

$$x_{ab} = \left(\frac{m_a}{m_a + m_b}\right) x_a + \left(\frac{m_b}{m_a + m_b}\right) x_b. \tag{3–14b}$$

The latter location is termed the *center of mass* of the pair of particles. From the first integration of Eq. (3–13), we obtain

$$m_a \dot{x}_a + m_b \dot{x}_b = m_{ab} \dot{x}_{ab} = \text{constant, independent of } t. \tag{3–15}$$

The quantity in Eq. (3–15) can be identified as the *total momentum* of the pair of particles. Under the action of mutual forces which are central, the total momentum of the pair is conserved. As a result, the *kinetic energy of the center of mass* is also conserved.

The total kinetic energy at any instant of time is

$$T_{x_a} + T_{x_b} = \tfrac{1}{2} m_a (\dot{x}_a)^2 + \tfrac{1}{2} m_b (\dot{x}_b)^2$$

$$= \frac{1}{2} m_{ab} (\dot{x}_{ab})^2 + \frac{1}{2} \left(\frac{m_a m_b}{m_a + m_b}\right) (\dot{x}_a - \dot{x}_b)^2. \tag{3–16}$$

The first term on the right side of this equation is the kinetic energy of the center of mass. The second term, involving the difference in the velocities of the particles, is referred to as the *kinetic energy of relative motion*. The quantity $[m_a m_b / (m_a + m_b)]$ is termed the *reduced mass* of the pair of particles.

An equation for the relative motion similar to Eq. (3–10) can be obtained from Eq. (3–12). We have, in general,

$$m_a m_b \ddot{x}_a = m_b f_{x_a}, \quad \text{and} \quad m_a m_b \ddot{x}_b = m_a f_{x_b}.$$

Hence, by Eq. (3–12), for central forces

$$m_a m_b (\ddot{x}_a - \ddot{x}_b) = (m_b + m_a) f_{x_b},$$

or

$$\left(\frac{m_a m_b}{m_a + m_b}\right) (\ddot{x}_a - \ddot{x}_b) = f_{x_a}. \tag{3–17}$$

Since the force f_{x_a} is, by hypothesis, a function only of the distance between the particles, $x_a - x_b$, we can apply the arguments leading to Eq. (3–10). Evidently we shall find that

$$\frac{1}{2} \left(\frac{m_a m_b}{m_a + m_b}\right) (\dot{x}_a - \dot{x}_b)^2 + V(x_b - x_a)$$

$$= \text{constant, independent of time,} \tag{3–18}$$

or that the *energy of relative motion* of two particles subjected only to central forces is a constant of their motion. The total energy, consisting of the sum of the energy of relative motion and the kinetic energy of the center of mass, is also a constant of the motion.

The kinetic energy of relative motion can be written in a form which is of more general utility than that given in Eq. (3–16). We have

$$\tfrac{1}{2}m_a(\dot{x}_a - \dot{x}_{ab})^2 + \tfrac{1}{2}m_b(\dot{x}_b - \dot{x}_{ab})^2$$

$$= \tfrac{1}{2}m_a(\dot{x}_a)^2 - m_a\dot{x}_a\dot{x}_{ab} + \tfrac{1}{2}m_a(\dot{x}_{ab})^2$$

$$+ \tfrac{1}{2}m_b(\dot{x}_b)^2 - m_b\dot{x}_b\dot{x}_{ab} + \tfrac{1}{2}m_b(\dot{x}_{ab})^2$$

$$= \tfrac{1}{2}m_a(\dot{x}_a)^2 + \tfrac{1}{2}m_b(\dot{x}_b)^2 - \tfrac{1}{2}m_{ab}(\dot{x}_{ab})^2, \tag{3–19}$$

where Eqs. (3–14a) and (3–14b) have been employed. In this form, a comparison with Eq. (3–16) reveals that the kinetic energy of relative motion is expressible as the sum of the kinetic energies of the individual particles *relative to their center of mass.*

The relations we have exhibited in Eqs. (3–15), (3–18), and (3–19) are easily generalized. For any number of particles subject only to inter-particle forces which are central (i.e., derivable from a potential energy function which depends only upon the distances between the particles), both the total momentum and total energy of the system are *conserved* and constant with the passage of time. Whatever the nature of the forces, however, the kinetic energy of a system can always be expressed as the sum of the kinetic energy of its center of mass and the kinetic energies of the individual particles moving relative to the center of mass. We shall not derive these relations, but will leave them to be demonstrated by the interested reader.

A further important extension of the previous relations is worth examining. This extension relates to the *dimensionality* of the space in which the particles move. The special case we have considered deals with one-dimensional motion. Realistically, the motion of particles can be resolved into three mutually perpendicular directions, of which we have considered only one. Experience yields the result that Newton's Laws of Motion, expressed in Eq. (3–3), are applicable to each mutually perpendicular direction. Hence, equations identical to those we have examined apply to each direction as well. We need only to relabel the directions. Thus, in terms of a coordinate system of cartesian axes, we will have

$$f_y(t) = ma_y(t) \tag{3–20}$$

for motion in the *y*-direction and

$$f_z(t) = ma_z(t) \tag{3–21}$$

for motion in the z-direction. The force components (f_x, f_y, f_z) and the acceleration components (a_x, a_y, a_z) refer to the cartesian axes.

The equations of motion can be combined into a single vector equation, as we have illustrated in Section 2 of the previous chapter. We obtain for a single particle

$$\mathbf{f} = m\mathbf{a},$$

or, in terms of the position vector $\mathbf{r}$ of the particle,

$$\mathbf{f} = m\ddot{\mathbf{r}},$$

with the components being those indicated above. The vector equation is to be understood as an abbreviation for three equations.

Although the equations of motion, Eqs. (3–3), (3–20), and (3–21), are said to be *independent* of one another, they may be related if the components of force depend upon one another in some way. Just such a relation occurs when the interparticle force depends only upon the *spatial distance* between the particles. To see this, let us consider an interparticle potential energy function

$$V = V(r_{ab}) = V(\sqrt{(x_a - x_b)^2 + (y_a - y_b)^2 + (z_a - z_b)^2}),$$

since

$$r_{ab} = \sqrt{(x_a - x_b)^2 + (y_a - y_b)^2 + (z_a - z_b)^2}.$$

We can write down three equations for particle a:

$$\left. \begin{aligned} -V'(r_{ab}) \frac{(x_a - x_b)}{r_{ab}} &= m\ddot{x}_a, \\[1em] -V'(r_{ab}) \frac{(y_a - y_b)}{r_{ab}} &= m\ddot{y}_a, \\[1em] -V'(r_{ab}) \frac{(z_a - z_b)}{r_{ab}} &= m\ddot{z}_a. \end{aligned} \right\} \tag{3–22}$$

A similar set of equations, in which the subscripts a and b are interchanged, holds for particle b. (Note that $r_{ab} = r_{ba}$.) It is easily verified that Eq. (3–13), with analogous equations in the y- and z-components, is obtained. To obtain the analog of Eq. (3–18), we proceed somewhat indirectly: we construct the total relative energy and verify its constancy in time. Thus we examine the time derivative of the total energy of relative motion, E_R:

$$\frac{dE_R}{dt} = \frac{d}{dt}\left[\frac{\mu}{2}(\dot{x}_a - \dot{x}_b)^2 + \frac{\mu}{2}(\dot{y}_a - \dot{y}_b)^2 + \frac{\mu}{2}(\dot{z}_a - \dot{z}_b)^2 + V(r_{ab}) \right],$$

where we have represented the reduced mass of the system by μ. Keeping in mind that all components of the position of both particles are implicit functions of the time, we obtain

$$\frac{dE_R}{dt} = \mu[(\dot{x}_a - \dot{x}_b)(\ddot{x}_a - \ddot{x}_b) + (\dot{y}_a - \dot{y}_b)(\ddot{y}_a - \ddot{y}_b) + (\dot{z}_a - \dot{z}_b)(\ddot{z}_a - \ddot{z}_b)]$$

$$+ V'(r_{ab})\left[\frac{(x_a - x_b)}{r_{ab}}(\dot{x}_a - \dot{x}_b)\right.$$

$$\left.+ \frac{(y_a - y_b)}{r_{ab}}(\dot{y}_a - \dot{y}_b) + \frac{(z_a - z_b)}{r_{ab}}(\dot{z}_a - \dot{z}_b)\right]$$

$$= 0,$$

by Eqs. (3–22). Hence

$$\frac{\mu}{2}[(\dot{x}_a - \dot{x}_b)^2 + (\dot{y}_a - \dot{y}_b)^2 + (\dot{z}_a - \dot{z}_b)^2] + V(r_{ab})$$

$$= \text{constant, independent of time.} \quad (3\text{–}23)$$

Because the kinetic energy of the center of mass also is a constant of the motion of the particles, so too is the total energy of the system.

In terms of three-dimensional motion of particles, other constants of their motion also occur. For example, for a particle subjected to a conservative force arising from a potential function which depends solely upon the distance of the particle from the *origin* (a so-called *central field potential*),

$$V = V(r) = V(\sqrt{x^2 + y^2 + z^2}),$$

we consider the quantity

$$\frac{d}{dt}\{xp_y - yp_x\} = \dot{x}p_y + x\dot{p}_y - \dot{y}p_x - y\dot{p}_x = x\dot{p}_y - y\dot{p}_x,$$

by the definition of momentum. By Eqs. (3–4) and (3–9), we have

$$\dot{p}_x = -\frac{\partial V(r)}{\partial x} = -V'(r)\frac{x}{r},$$

$$\dot{p}_y = -\frac{\partial V(r)}{\partial y} = -V'(r)\frac{y}{r}.$$

Hence,

$$\frac{d}{dt}\{xp_y - yp_x\} = 0;$$

also, by interchanging the labels of the coordinate axes, we write

$$\frac{d}{dt}\{yp_z - zp_y\} = \frac{d}{dt}\{zp_x - xp_z\} = 0.$$

The three constant quantities which have been exhibited are the *components of angular momentum* of a particle. The extension to several particles moving with respect to their common center of mass is made readily, but we shall not do so.

The constants of motion enable us to determine certain aspects of the motion of particles relatively easily. This situation occurs in the process of *collisions* between pairs of particles. To illustrate the procedure, we may assume that a central force exists between the particles and that this force vanishes when the interparticle distance exceeds some fixed value. Before the particles collide (i.e., when they are moving toward each other at a distance exceeding the "range" of the forces acting upon them), they will have initial momenta $\mathbf{p}_a(i)$ and $\mathbf{p}_b(i)$. After collision (i.e., when they are moving away from each other at a distance exceeding the range of the forces acting upon them) they will have final momenta $\mathbf{p}_a(f)$ and $\mathbf{p}_b(f)$. Conservation of momentum requires that

$$\mathbf{p}_a(i) + \mathbf{p}_b(i) = \mathbf{p}_a(f) + \mathbf{p}_b(f).$$

This relation is expressed more conveniently in terms of the center of mass of the system. However, before doing so, we may simplify matters by choosing a set of cartesian axes such that the initial trajectories of the two particles lie, say, in the xy-plane. Then the initial z-components of momentum vanish. Hence the sum of the final z-components of momentum also must vanish. Now, as in Eq. (3–17), we must have

$$\frac{m_a m_b}{m_a + m_b} (\ddot{z}_a - \ddot{z}_b) = f_{z,a}.$$

A central force $f_{z,a}$ derivable from a potential energy function which depends only upon the interparticle distance has the form

$$f_{z,a} = - \frac{\partial V(r_{ab})}{\partial z_a}$$

$$= -V'(r_{ab}) \frac{(z_a - z_b)}{r_{ab}}.$$

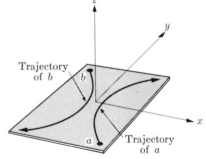

Fig. 3–1. Choice of coordinates in planar motion of two particles.

Hence for particles in the xy-plane the force vanishes, so that the motion is confined to the plane. It can be represented by Fig. 3–1.

The choice has been made here of a *coplanar* collision. This is not the general state of affairs prevailing among molecular collisions, but for collisions with a zero value for the angular momentum, this is necessarily true. These collisions are the ones about to be discussed. Nevertheless, planar collisions having nonzero values of the angular momentum are also possible, but only if the ranges of the forces of interaction are not vanishingly small.

We may now express the conservation of momentum in terms of the center of mass. We have for planar collisions

$$\dot{x}_{ab}(i) = \dot{x}_{ab}(f), \tag{3–24a}$$

$$\dot{y}_{ab}(i) = \dot{y}_{ab}(f), \tag{3–24b}$$

$$\dot{z}_{ab}(i) = \dot{z}_{ab}(f) = 0. \tag{3–24c}$$

From Eq. (3–14b), and an analogous one for the y-component, we see that for both initial and final values

$$m_a(\dot{x}_a - \dot{x}_{ab}) + m_b(\dot{x}_b - \dot{x}_{ab}) = 0, \tag{3–25a}$$

$$m_a(\dot{y}_a - \dot{y}_{ab}) + m_b(\dot{y}_b - \dot{y}_{ab}) = 0. \tag{3–25b}$$

Hence, the momentum of motion relative to the center of mass vanishes both before and after the collision.

From these equations, we see that

$$\frac{m_a}{2}[(\dot{x}_a - \dot{x}_{ab})^2 + (\dot{y}_a - \dot{y}_{ab})^2] = \left(\frac{m_b}{m_a}\right) \cdot \frac{m_b}{2}[(\dot{x}_b - \dot{x}_{ab})^2 + (\dot{y}_b - \dot{y}_{ab})^2],$$

or

$$T_{R,a} = \left(\frac{m_b}{m_a}\right) T_{R,b}$$

for both initial and final values. Hence,

$$\frac{T_{R,a}(i)}{T_{R,b}(i)} = \frac{T_{R,a}(f)}{T_{R,b}(f)} = \frac{m_b}{m_a}, \tag{3–26}$$

so that the ratio of the kinetic energies of the two particles relative to their center of mass also is the same before and after the collision.

If we now assume that the "range" of the interparticle forces is small, we see that over almost all of the trajectory the total energy is entirely kinetic energy. Since the kinetic energy of the center of mass is conserved, we have, by Eq. (3–19),

$$T_{R,a}(i) + T_{R,b}(i) = T_{R,a}(f) + T_{R,b}(f). \tag{3–27}$$

With Eq. (3–26) this implies that

$$T_{R,a}(i)\left[1 + \frac{T_{R,b}(i)}{T_{R,a}(i)}\right] = T_{R,a}(f)\left[1 + \frac{T_{R,b}(f)}{T_{R,a}(f)}\right],$$

or

$$T_{R,a}(i) = T_{R,a}(f).$$

That is, the kinetic energies of the individual particles relative to their center of mass, and hence the magnitudes of the corresponding momenta of each particle, are also the same before and after the collision.

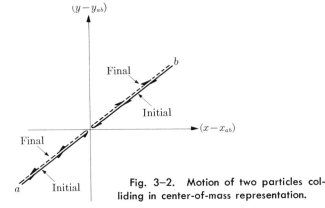

Fig. 3–2. Motion of two particles colliding in center-of-mass representation.

In terms of a nonrotating plane which moves with the center of mass of the system, the motion is extremely simple. In such a moving coordinate system, the corresponding components of the momenta of the particles are equal in magnitude and of opposite sense, as indicated by Eqs. (3–25). We can represent the motion as a "head-on" collision of the two particles. Since the particles are assumed to be impenetrable, they simply reverse their direction after such a collision. Again, they must have components which differ from each other only in sign. We have seen that the effect of the collision is to leave the magnitude of the individual components unaltered. This is indicated diagrammatically in Fig. 3–2. Hence we may conclude that after a head-on collision

$$\dot{x}_a(f) - \dot{x}_{ab} = -\dot{x}_a(i) + \dot{x}_{ab}$$

and

$$\dot{y}_a(f) - \dot{y}_{ab} = -\dot{y}_a(i) + \dot{y}_{ab},$$

(3–28)

with identical relations for the particle b. Since $\dot{x}_{ab}$ is known from the initial values, we have finally

$$\dot{x}_a(f) = -\dot{x}_a(i) + 2\left[\left(\frac{m_a}{m_a + m_b}\right)\dot{x}_a(i) + \left(\frac{m_b}{m_a + m_b}\right)\dot{x}_b(i)\right],$$

$$= \left(\frac{m_a - m_b}{m_a + m_b}\right)\dot{x}_a(i) + \left(\frac{2m_b}{m_a + m_b}\right)\dot{x}_b(i).$$

(3–29)

Similarly,

$$\dot{y}_a(f) = \left(\frac{m_a - m_b}{m_a + m_b}\right)\dot{y}_a(i) + \left(\frac{2m_b}{m_a + m_b}\right)\dot{y}_b(i).$$

(3–30)

Also, we can obtain

$$\dot{x}_b(f) = \left(\frac{2m_a}{m_a + m_b}\right)\dot{x}_a(i) + \left(\frac{m_b - m_a}{m_b + m_a}\right)\dot{x}_b(i) \qquad (3\text{-}31)$$

and

$$\dot{y}_b(f) = \left(\frac{2m_a}{m_b + m_a}\right)\dot{y}_a(i) + \left(\frac{m_b - m_a}{m_b + m_a}\right)\dot{y}_b(i). \qquad (3\text{-}32)$$

Although the foregoing equations represent the general solution of the collision problem for two mass-points with zero-range interaction, they are sufficiently complicated to merit an examination of some simple cases. Perhaps some feeling for the changes resulting from such collisions can be obtained as a result. To simplify matters, we restrict our attention to cases in which one of the particles is initially at rest. Specifically, we consider collisions for which

$$\dot{x}_b(i) = \dot{y}_b(i) = \dot{y}_a(i) = 0.$$

Then, from Eqs. (3-29) and (3-31),

$$\dot{x}_a(f) = \left(\frac{m_a - m_b}{m_a + m_b}\right)\dot{x}_a(i),$$

$$\dot{x}_b(f) = \left(\frac{2m_a}{m_a + m_b}\right)\dot{x}_a(i).$$

Hence,

$$\frac{T_a(f)}{T_a(i)} = \left(\frac{m_a - m_b}{m_a + m_b}\right)^2 \qquad (3\text{-}33)$$

and

$$\frac{T_b(f)}{T_a(i)} = \frac{4m_a m_b}{(m_a + m_b)^2}. \qquad (3\text{-}34)$$

Equation (3-34) expresses the fraction of initial energy which is transferred to the second particle. It is plotted in Fig. 3-3. The maximum,

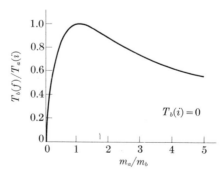

Fig. 3-3. Kinetic energy transfer as a function of colliding masses.

complete transfer occurs for equal masses. No transfer of energy occurs if the stationary particle has zero or infinite mass. In the latter case, the initial particle is completely reversed and leaves the collision with the same kinetic energy as it had originally.

As another case, we consider a head-on collision for which

$$\dot{x}_a(i) = -\dot{x}_b(i)$$

and

$$\dot{y}_a(i) = \dot{y}_b(f) = 0.$$

We obtain from Eqs. (3–29) and (3–31)

$$\dot{x}_a(f) = \left(\frac{m_a - 3m_b}{m_a + m_b}\right) \dot{x}_a(i)$$

and

$$\dot{x}_b(f) = \left(\frac{m_b - 3m_a}{m_a + m_b}\right) \dot{x}_b(i).$$

Hence,

$$\frac{T_a(f)}{T_a(i)} = \left(\frac{m_a - 3m_b}{m_a + m_b}\right)^2 \tag{3-35}$$

and

$$\frac{T_b(f)}{T_b(i)} = \left(\frac{m_b - 3m_a}{m_a + m_b}\right)^2. \tag{3-36}$$

Combining these two equations, we obtain also

$$\frac{T_a(f)}{T_b(f)} = \left(\frac{m_a - 3m_b}{m_b - 3m_a}\right)^2 \frac{T_a(i)}{T_b(i)}. \tag{3-37}$$

From these equations we see that a complete transfer of energy occurs [i.e., $T_a(f) = 0$] for some mass ratio. This occurs when

$$\frac{m_b}{m_a} = \frac{1}{3}.$$

It also occurs [i.e., $T_b(f) = 0$] when

$$\frac{m_a}{m_b} = \frac{1}{3}.$$

For equal masses the kinetic energy of each particle is unaltered by the collision.

Other cases may be examined, but these will be left for the interested student.

It will be noticed that our restriction to the motion of the center of mass of particles has left unattended their *internal motion*. As long as one deals with

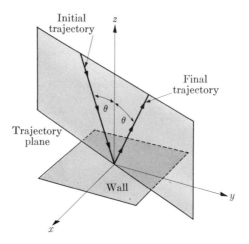

Fig. 3–4. Trajectory of particle colliding with a wall.

particles which can interact in a manner that depends only upon their mutual distances (of their respective centers of mass), no reference needs to be made to their internal motion. Under the stated conditions, the internal motion of the particles is completely independent of and unrelated to the motion of their centers of mass. Their behavior is then identical with that of the structureless particles we have tacitly assumed above. For reasons of simplicity, we shall assume that the particles with which we deal are of the sort described. In this case, their "size" needs elaboration; this is done in Chapter 5.

We conclude this lengthy review of the mechanics of particles by considering their collisions with *walls*. In idealized terms, a wall is a plane having a fixed location in space. For any real wall, such as that provided by a container for gases, the surface exposed to the gas is rarely planar on a macroscopic level; it certainly is not planar on a microscopic level. Neither is any real wall immovable. However, as compared with molecular sizes, these idealizations appear reasonable.

The trajectory of a mass-point approaching a wall is indicated schematically in Fig. 3–4. We may identify the wall with the xy-plane. Now, what mechanical quantities of the particles are conserved? To answer this question, we must specify the forces of interaction between the particle and the wall. It seems to be a fair statement that it depends only upon the distance between them. (Any other dependence would imply a variation of force over the *surface* of the wall. This may occur, but we need not consider it for our purposes. To be precise, we restrict our attention to *uniform walls*.) Hence, we assume that the force of interaction is derivable from a potential

$$V = V(z). \tag{3–38}$$

From Eqs. (3–5) and (3–9) we immediately conclude that the x- and y-components of momentum are conserved, and this means that the corresponding components of velocity are also constants of the motion.

For the z-component of velocity, we must consider the possible motion of the wall. However, to simplify matters we will suppose that any force exerted upon the wall by a colliding particle is balanced perfectly by an external opposite force. The net force being then zero, no motion of the wall occurs. In this way, Eq. (3–38) is applicable. For the motion in the z-direction, we now can make use of an equation analogous to Eq. (3–10). We have

$$T_z(t_2) + V[z(t_2)] = T_z(t_1) + V[z(t_1)].$$

If, now, we choose t_1 and t_2 to be such that they correspond to locations of the particle on the trajectory before and after collision and such that these locations are at distances greater than the range of the forces, we must have the total kinetic energy of the particle conserved for parts of the trajectory outside the range of the forces due to the wall. Hence

$$[\dot{z}(f)]^2 = [\dot{z}(i)]^2.$$

Since the z-component of velocity must reverse in direction as the result of the collision, we have

$$\dot{z}(f) = -\dot{z}(i). \tag{3–39}$$

From the conservation of the x- and y-components of velocity and Eq. (3–39), we are able to picture the trajectory of an *elastic collision* of a particle with a wall as moving in a plane perpendicular to the wall. If another plane is erected perpendicular to the wall and the trajectory plane, the initial trajectory reflects through the third plane to coincide with the final trajectory. The motion on one line is in the reverse sense of the other. These relations are depicted in Fig. 3–4.

From Eqs. (3–5) and (3–39) and the definition of momentum, we see that the impulse I imparted *to* the particle as the result of the collision is

$$I = \int_{t_1}^{t_2} dt\, f_z(t) = p_z(f) - p_z(i) = -2p_z(i).$$

Note that $p_z(i)$ must be negative if the particle is to collide with the wall. Hence, the impulse imparted to the particle is in a direction *away* from the wall. From the point of view of the wall, an impulse of the same sense must be applied to keep it stationary. Hence, the external impulse is

$$I_{\text{ext}} = -2p_z(i). \tag{3–40}$$

This impulse is applied *normal* to the (interior) surface of the wall.

3. EQUATION OF STATE OF UNIFORM IDEAL GASES

The pressure exerted by uniform ideal gases can be equated to the pressure required to keep the (free) walls of its container from moving. By Eq. (1–1), this pressure is simply related to the force which must be applied to the wall. We therefore seek to determine this force as a consequence of the assumptions we have stated previously. (Statements 2 and 5 in Section 1 of the present chapter.)

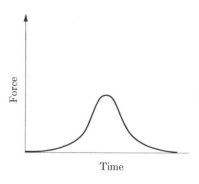

Fig. 3–5. Force-time curve for collision of particles with wall.

We have seen that a particle colliding with a stationary wall imparts an impulse to it which must be exactly balanced by an external impulse. If we could measure the force associated with the latter, we should have, schematically, the behavior indicated in Fig. 3–5. The actual shape of the curve is dependent upon the potential $V(z)$; nevertheless, whatever its shape, its area is given by Eq. (3–40). To deal with the model of an ideal gas, consideration must be given to the occurrence of many collisions, as suggested by Fig. 3–6. (Different shapes will arise from particles of different masses. We are assuming here that all particles are identical.) If these collisions are sufficiently numerous *and not coincident*, a fair measure of the force they will impart to the wall is their *time-average* value. This is made all the more reasonable because the uniform ideal gas is assumed to be in a stationary state; hence there is a continual bombardment of the wall by particles. In any fixed large interval of time, we expect essentially the same number of collisions.

Fig. 3–6. Force-time curve for several collisions of particles with wall.

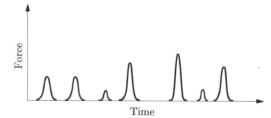

The introduction of a time-average value is an added assumption of the theory, to be sure. However, it differs from those we already have stated in an important way. It relates to the more general question of what theoretical quantities correspond to measured properties of a system. For this reason, the assumption pertains to the nature of the measurement itself. In the present case, formal justification for the time-average force can be obtained by requiring that the wall be subjected to a constant force of such a value that it will remain stationary in *an average sense*. Since this force imparts an impulse to the wall which is proportional to the interval of time for which it acts, while a steady rate of collisions does exactly the same, we are requiring that the *long-term* impulse imparted to the wall by colliding molecules be balanced by the impulse applied externally.

To express these ideas in mathematical terms, we consider a time interval $(t_2 - t_1)$ which is sufficiently large to assure that a large number of collisions with the wall have occurred. During that time interval virtually no collisions between particles will have occurred, since the model supposes the particles to have no spatial extension. If there are N collisions occurring upon an area A of the wall in this time interval, the time-average value of the pressure is

$$P = \frac{\bar{F}}{A} = \frac{(I_1)_{\text{ext}} + (I_2)_{\text{ext}} + \cdots + (I_N)_{\text{ext}}}{(t_2 - t_1)A}$$

$$= \sum_{k=1}^{N} \frac{(I_k)_{\text{ext}}}{(t_2 - t_1)A} = -\sum_{k=1}^{N} \frac{2p_{z,k}(i)}{(t_2 - t_1)A} \qquad (3\text{-}41)$$

by Eq. (3-40); the sum indicated is over the N molecules which collide with the wall during the time interval in question.

In Eq. (3-41), we have made use of a *definition* of an average value of a function, as follows. If $f(x)$ is a function of x, the average value of the function in the interval is defined as that value which multiplies the interval to yield the integral of the function in that interval. That is,

$$(x_2 - x_1)\bar{f} = \int_{x_1}^{x_2} dx\, f(x).$$

Sometimes, more generally, we define a weighted average as

$$\bar{f} = \frac{\displaystyle\int_{x_1}^{x_2} dx\, w(x)f(x)}{\displaystyle\int_{x_1}^{x_2} dx\, w(x)}.$$

To evaluate the sum in Eq. (3-41), we need to know two things: (1) the number of molecules N colliding in the time interval $(t_2 - t_1)$, and (2) the various values of $p_{z,k}(i)$ of the colliding molecules. To estimate the former, we first group the various colliding molecules according to the value of

$p_z(i)$ they have. Let $n(p_z)$ be the number of all those having the value p_z (we drop the reference to initial value, for simplicity) which collide in the stated time interval. Then we may write

$$P = - \sum_{\text{all } p_z \leq 0} \frac{2n(p_z)}{A} \frac{p_z}{t_2 - t_1},$$ (3–42)

such that

$$\sum_{\text{all } p_z \leq 0} n(p_z) = N.$$ (3–43)

The sum must be taken over all molecules which approach the wall; hence $p_z \leq 0$. The sums in Eqs. (3–42) and (3–43) are to be understood as purely *formal* operations: we intend to add the contributions of each group of molecules. When, as actually is the case, p_z is not limited to discrete sets of values but may take on any value in a continuous range, the sums are to be replaced by integrals. This replacement will be considered in detail in the succeeding chapter. For the present, however, the sums will be used for reasons of simplicity of notation. The idea involved is unaltered by the use of sums or integrals.

The various $n(p_z)$ can be estimated as follows. Since they all collide with a unit area of the wall in a time interval $(t_2 - t_1)$, they must all come from a volume in the gas equal to the product of the distance of the farthest one from the wall and the area of collision. Since the farthest distance such a molecule can have is determined from the product of the z-component of its velocity and the time interval, we obtain

$$V(p_z) = -A \cdot (t_2 - t_1)(p_z/m).$$

The basis for this expression is indicated in Fig. 3–7. Because the ideal gas is uniform, there will be a constant density of particles having a prescribed value of p_z. Calling its value $\rho(p_z)$, we have

$$n(p_z) = \rho(p_z)V(p_z) = -\rho(p_z) \cdot A \cdot (t_2 - t_1)(p_z/m).$$

With this expression, we obtain

$$P = \sum_{\text{all } p_z \leq 0} 2\rho(p_z)(p_z^2/m),$$ (3–44)

and

$$N = -(t_2 - t_1)A \sum_{\text{all } p_z \leq 0} \rho(p_z)(p_z/m).$$ (3–45)

Once we know $\rho(p_z)$ for all values of p_z, the solution to our problem is at hand. However, this quantity requires further analysis.

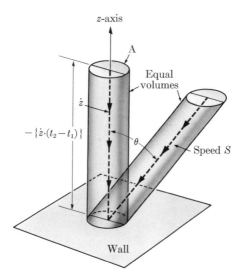

Fig. 3-7. Relations between swept-out volume and impacting particles.

For the present, we may dispense with the needed analysis to simplify the relations obtained. We notice, first of all, that according to the assumption of isotropy

$$\rho(p_z) = \rho(-p_z)$$

and hence

$$\sum_{\text{all } p_z \leq 0} \rho(p_z) = \frac{1}{2} \sum_{\text{all } p_z} \rho(p_z) = \tfrac{1}{2}\rho = \frac{1}{2}\frac{n}{V}, \tag{3-46}$$

one-half the total number of molecules per unit of volume. We may thus express the total pressure as an *average over the molecules* of the quantity (p_z^2/m). We write

$$P = \frac{\sum_{\text{all } p_z \leq 0} 2\rho(p_z)(p_z^2/m)}{\sum_{\text{all } p_z \leq 0} 2\rho(p_z)} \cdot \sum_{\text{all } p_z \leq 0} 2\rho(p_z)$$

$$= \rho \cdot \left\{ \frac{\sum_{\text{all } p_z} \rho(p_z)(p_z^2/m)}{\sum_{\text{all } p_z} \rho(p_z)} \right\} = 2\rho \cdot \overline{p_z^2/2m}. \tag{3-47}$$

In Eq. (3-47) we have introduced the *discrete analog* of a weighted average. Thus, we define such an average as

$$\bar{f} = \frac{\sum_{n=1}^{\infty} w_n f_n}{\sum_{n=1}^{\infty} w_n}.$$

The formal similarity between sums and integrals makes the relations simple to remember.

The quantity $\overline{(p_z^2/2m)}$ is the average value of the kinetic energy in the z-direction *per molecule*. Again, because of isotropy, the corresponding average value of the kinetic energy in the x- and y-directions must be the same. That is,

$$\overline{p_x^2/2m} = \overline{p_y^2/2m} = \overline{p_z^2/2m}. \tag{3–48}$$

Calling the average total kinetic energy per molecule

$$\bar{\epsilon} = \frac{\overline{p_x^2 + p_y^2 + p_z^2}}{2m}, \tag{3–49}$$

we obtain the important result

$$P = \tfrac{2}{3}\rho\bar{\epsilon} = \frac{2}{3}\frac{n\bar{\epsilon}}{V}, $$

or

$$PV = \tfrac{2}{3}n\bar{\epsilon}. \tag{3–50}$$

The similarity with Eq. (1–13) is noteworthy. Here, however, the quantity n is the number of molecules, while m/W is the number of gram-moles. To conform to our present notation, we should replace m by (nm), the latter m referring to the mass of a single molecule. In the same way, we introduce *Avogadro's number*, N_0, so that

$$W = N_0 m.$$

With these changes, the equation of state of an ideal gas becomes

$$PV = \frac{n}{N_0} RT. \tag{3–51}$$

To be consistent, we must have the consequence that

$$\bar{\epsilon} = \frac{3}{2}\left(\frac{R}{N_0}\right) T, \tag{3–52}$$

or that the average kinetic energy per molecule of an ideal gas is proportional to the absolute temperature and is *independent of the kind of molecule*. The quantity

$$k \equiv \left(\frac{R}{N_0}\right) \tag{3–53}$$

is called *Boltzmann's constant*.

Although for reasons of simplicity we have restricted our attention to pure ideal gases, the extension to mixtures offers no difficulty. We need only to keep the different molecules distinct and repeat the previous analysis for each kind. Because of the direct mechanical connection between

TABLE 3–1

HEAT CAPACITIES AT CONSTANT VOLUME
FOR TWO NOBLE GASES AT 15°C

Gas	C_V, cal/gm-mole·°K
He	3.00
Ar	3.06

the contribution of each sort of molecule and the total average impulse, the obvious nature of Dalton's Law of Partial Pressures [Eq. (1–21)] emerges. All the properties of the ideal gas we have already discussed in Chapter 1 are thus direct consequences of the mechanical model we have assumed.

However, one thing new has been added. Because of Eq. (3–52), we see that the *internal energy of an ideal gas of mass-points* is (per gram-mole)

$$E = N_0\bar{\epsilon} = \tfrac{3}{2}RT. \qquad (3\text{--}54)$$

If we attempt to increase the temperature of such a gas by adding *heat* to it, we necessarily change the internal energy of the gas. If this heat is added while the volume of the gas is kept fixed, the ratio of the change in energy (i.e., heat, in the present case) to the change in temperature is the heat capacity at constant volume,

$$C_V \equiv \lim_{\substack{\Delta E \to 0 \\ \Delta T \to 0}} \left(\frac{\Delta E}{\Delta T}\right)_V = \left(\frac{\partial E}{\partial T}\right)_V = \tfrac{3}{2}R. \qquad (3\text{--}55)$$

It is remarkable that the quantity R, introduced originally in terms of the equation of state of an ideal gas, is also involved in its purely *caloric* behavior. In Table 3–1 we give heat capacities for two of the noble gases. As we shall see later, these substances should illustrate Eq. (3–55) rather well. In terms of the mechanical equivalent of heat,

$$1 \text{ calorie} \eqsim 4.1855 \text{ joule} \eqsim 4.1855 \times 10^7 \text{ ergs}, \qquad (3\text{--}56)$$

we can obtain, as indicated in Chapter 1, that

$$R = 1.9865 \text{ cal/gm-mole·°K.}$$

Hence, for an ideal gas of mass-points, we should expect

$$C_V = 2.980 \text{ cal/gm-mole·°K.}$$

This result, it is to be noted, is independent of the kind of gas.

Whereas a relation like Eq. (3–51) is referred to as a *thermal equation of state*, one like Eq. (3–54) is referred to as a *caloric equation of state*. The total equilibrium behavior of the uniform ideal gas is obtained from a knowledge of these two equations and the principles of thermodynamics.

4. EFFUSION

We are now in a position to make an estimate of the speeds with which molecules of an ideal gas move. From Eqs. (3–52) and (3–53), we can obtain

$$\bar{\epsilon} = \frac{m}{2}\overline{\dot{x}^2 + \dot{y}^2 + \dot{z}^2} = \tfrac{3}{2}kT. \tag{3–57}$$

The quantity

$$S = \sqrt{\dot{x}^2 + \dot{y}^2 + \dot{z}^2}$$

is the *speed* of a molecule. Hence, rewriting, we have

$$\bar{\epsilon} = \frac{m}{2}\overline{S^2},$$

and

$$\sqrt{\overline{S^2}} = \sqrt{\frac{3kT}{m}} = \sqrt{\frac{3RT}{W}}. \tag{3–58}$$

The quantity on the left of the equation is termed the *root-mean-square* speed, i.e., the square *root* of the *mean* of the *square* of the speed. It is not identical with the mean speed, as we shall later see, but is quite close in value to it. If we substitute numbers, we shall obtain

$$R = 82.057\,\frac{cm^3 \cdot atm}{gm\text{-}mole \cdot {}^\circ K} \times 1.01325 \times 10^6\,\frac{dynes}{cm^2 \cdot atm} \times \frac{1\,gm \cdot cm}{sec^2 \cdot dyne}$$

$$= 83.144 \times 10^6 \left(\frac{cm}{sec}\right)^2 \frac{gm}{gm\text{-}mole \cdot {}^\circ K}.$$

Thus, if T is the absolute temperature and W the usual molecular weight in gm/gm-mole, we have

$$\sqrt{\overline{S^2}} = 1.581 \times 10^4 \sqrt{\frac{T}{W}}\,\frac{cm}{sec}$$

$$= 353 \sqrt{\frac{T}{W}}\,\frac{miles}{hour}. \tag{3–59}$$

With speeds of the order of magnitude indicated, it is not surprising to have extraordinarily large diffusivities. Nevertheless, the diffusivities are finite for the ideal gas.

The enormous speeds to be associated with molecular motion in gases implies that the rate at which collisions occur with the walls of any vessel containing a gas also is large. To estimate this value, we return to Eq. (3–45). We define the *collision rate per unit area,*

$$\bar{\nu} \equiv \frac{N}{(t_2 - t_1)A} = - \sum_{\text{all } p_z \leq 0} \rho(p_z)\frac{p_z}{m}. \tag{3–60}$$

As previously, we rearrange this equation to give

$$\bar{\nu} = - \frac{\sum_{\text{all } p_z \leq 0} \rho(p_z)p_z/m}{\sum_{\text{all } p_z \leq 0} \rho(p_z)} \cdot \sum_{\text{all } p_z \leq 0} \rho(p_z)$$

$$= \tfrac{1}{2}\rho \cdot \frac{\sum_{\text{all } p_z} \rho(p_z)|p_z|/m}{\sum_{\text{all } p_z} \rho(p_z)}$$

$$= \tfrac{1}{2}\rho \, \overline{\left|\frac{p_z}{m}\right|} = \tfrac{1}{2}\rho\overline{|\dot{z}|}. \tag{3–61}$$

For a given density, the collision rate per unit area is proportional to the molecular average of the *magnitude* of the *velocity* in the direction of the wall.

To bring Eq. (3–61) into a more convenient form, we may again exploit the isotropy of the system. We must have, as a consequence,

$$\overline{|\dot{z}|} = \overline{|\dot{y}|} = \overline{|\dot{x}|}.$$

However, these relations are not especially useful. More useful is the fact that for any speed S, as indicated in Fig. 3–7, we have

$$\dot{z} = -S\cos\theta, \tag{3–62}$$

where θ is the angle made between the direction of the colliding molecule and the direction normal to the surface of the wall. In these terms, since S is always positive,

$$\overline{|\dot{z}|} = \overline{S|\cos\theta|}.$$

The explicit evaluation of this quantity requires a knowledge of $\rho(p_z)$. Nevertheless, we can anticipate certain results. Because of our assumption of isotropy, we recognize that all directions that a molecule may have are equally likely. If the previous averaging *over molecules* is regarded as an averaging over *directions* of the molecules followed by an averaging over the *speeds* of the molecules, we can make some simplification. Explicitly, the assumption of equal likelihood of any direction is identical with the statement that all values of $|\cos\theta|$ have equal likelihood. Since the latter quantity has values ranging from zero to unity, we seek the average of all such values. For each possible value of $|\cos \theta|$, say q, there is an equally likely value $(1 - q)$. The average of these two values is $\frac{1}{2}$. This average is independent of the value of q, so that the total sum of the equally likely values of $|\cos \theta|$ is one-half their number. Hence, the isotropy assumption yields

$$\overline{|\cos \theta|} = \tfrac{1}{2},$$

regardless of speed. As a result, we can obtain

$$\bar{\nu} = \tfrac{1}{4}\rho\bar{S}, \tag{3–63}$$

the collision frequency now being proportional to the *average speed* of a molecule.

Any further simplification of the expression for $\bar{\nu}$ requires a knowledge of $\bar{S}$. This evaluation will be dealt with later. As we already have noted, it is not identical with the root-mean-square speed. Nevertheless, we shall see that it is quite close to it in value. To state this mathematically, we write

$$\bar{S} = \alpha\sqrt{\overline{S^2}}, \tag{3–64}$$

and note that $\alpha \doteq 1$. Thereupon, we obtain

$$\bar{\nu} = \frac{\alpha}{4}\rho\sqrt{\overline{S^2}} = \frac{\alpha}{4}\rho\sqrt{\frac{3RT}{W}}. \tag{3–65}$$

From this expression, the collision frequency varies inversely with the molecular weight of the gas.

The expression we have obtained for the collision frequency is identical with the *effusion rate* for an ideal gas. If we imagine a small hole in the wall of a container enclosing a gas, with a vacuum on the other side of it, the molecules which otherwise would strike the region of the hole will pass through the hole. Provided that the hole permits the unimpeded passage of molecules entering it, the rate at which the molecules leave the parent gas is evidently equal to the rate at which collisions would have occurred. Experimentally, this requires that the thickness of the wall in the immediate vicinity of the hole be extremely small. Experiments bearing on this phenomenon were first carried out by Graham, who measured the mass of gas issuing through small perforations in a metal plate. The expression for the *mass-effusion* rate follows from Eq. (3–65). We have

$$\dot{m} = m\bar{\nu} = \frac{\alpha}{4}\left(\frac{mn}{V}\right)\sqrt{\frac{3RT}{W}}$$

$$= \frac{\alpha}{4}P\sqrt{\frac{3W}{RT}}, \tag{3–66}$$

TABLE 3–2

RELATIVE EFFUSION RATES AT FIXED PRESSURE
AND TEMPERATURE*

Gas	Relative effusion rate	$\sqrt{W/W_{air}}$
Air	1.000 (reference)	1.000
H_2	0.276	0.263
CH_4	0.753	0.745
N_2	0.986	0.986
O_2	1.053	1.051
CO_2	1.203	1.237

* Graham, *Phil. Trans. Roy. Soc.* **136,** 573 (1846).

so that the mass-effusion rate at fixed temperature and pressure is proportional to the molecular weight of the gas. In terms of numbers of molecules, of course, the effusion rate at fixed temperature and pressure is inversely proportional to the molecular weight. This was the relation determined by Graham, and is referred to as *Graham's Law of Effusion.* Some data pertinent to Eq. (3–66) are given in Table 3–2 for gases at the same temperature and pressure.

In spite of the accord between Eq. (3–66) and the data of Table 3–2, there is reason to doubt the relevance of the agreement. The effusion equation relates implicitly to the unimpeded flow of gas molecules through a hole in the wall of the vessel containing it. When the wall thickness is sufficiently small, this condition can be realized. However, any practical situation involves a nonzero thickness of the wall, so that some collisions of gas molecules with the sides of the resulting tube are bound to occur. When they do occur, the gaseous flow may be impeded. The lack of perfect agreement of the data of Table 3–2 with the theoretical predictions, in fact, points to the presence of such effects in the experiments. A more detailed analysis of the actual experiment must include the effect of nonzero sizes of the gas molecules and the distances between them, since the ultimate cause of the impeded flow can be traced to intermolecular collisions within the confines of the tube. The gas flow within the tube then acquires an aspect of viscous flow which will exhibit a molecular weight dependence similar to that observed in Table 3–2. (Viscous flow is discussed in Chapter 5.) Nevertheless, the precise validation of the effusion equation has been carried out by Knudsen, who managed to prepare adequately "thin holes" for gaseous effusion.

The use of Eq. (3–66) to determine the molecular weight of gases at small pressures is an interesting application of the elementary kinetic theory summarized by Graham's Law. However, an equally important use of this equation is in the determination of the vapor pressure of slightly volatile materials of known molecular weight. The method has been developed by Knudsen. The slightly volatile material is placed in a previously evacuated container which is then sealed, except for a small hole of known area. The container and contents are brought to a prescribed temperature and the surroundings evacuated. After the lapse of a measured interval of time, the container is cooled and again weighed. From the difference in weight, the molecular weight of the vapor, and the temperature, the pressure of the effusing gas is calculated.

In order to have an order-of-magnitude value for collision rates, we may evaluate Eq. (3–65) at standard conditions of temperature and pressure. Under these conditions

$$\rho_{STP} = 2.6870 \times 10^{19} \text{ molecules cm}^{-3}, \tag{3-67}$$

which is known also as the *Loschmidt* number. Hence,

$$\bar{\nu} = \alpha \frac{1.755 \times 10^{24}}{\sqrt{W}} \text{ collisions·sec}^{-1}·\text{cm}^{-2}, \tag{3-68}$$

an enormous number. For hydrogen it amounts roughly to two gram-moles striking one square centimeter of wall per second.

With Eqs. (3–51) and (3–63), we have completed an analysis of ideal gases in terms of a mechanical model of mass-points of negligible interaction. However, the analysis we have made has relied upon *identifications* mainly with the observed low-pressure behavior of gases through the equation of state of ideal gases and partially through the effusion rates observed for real gases. Much detail needs to be supplied to complete the theory. Thus, we need a value for the average speed of a molecule as compared with the root-mean-square speed. We need, furthermore, to deal with real gases, especially with regard to the feature of nonzero molecular size. To these questions we now turn.

5. SUMMARY

The molecular features of an ideal gas have been traced to certain of the general properties of gases at small values of the pressure. We have stressed how the large diffusivities of such gases, their isotropy, and their stationary behavior lead intuitively to a mechanical model of mass-points with which to represent the ideal gas.

As essential assumption of the model, apart from various idealizations, is that the molecules exhibit motions satisfying Newton's equations. These have been reviewed at some length. Particular attention has been directed to the constants of motion of simple collections of particles. The use of these quantities in solving simple binary mass-point collisions has been indicated.

The uniform ideal gas has been examined from the viewpoint of a collection of noninteracting mass-points which collide with the walls of their container. The pressure exerted by such a gas is related to the time-average of the impulse imparted by collisions to the wall. The observed thermal equation of state is obtained when an identification is made of the mean kinetic energy of a molecule and a quantity proportional to the absolute temperature of the ideal gas. The caloric behavior of ideal (monatomic) gases has been obtained as a result. The effusive behavior of the ideal gas provides another test of the model by exhibiting Graham's Law of Effusion as a consequence of the analysis.

EXERCISES

1. Consider a particle of mass m confined to motion in a straight line and subjected to a force $f_x = -K \sin(\alpha t)$. Assume that it is to be found at $x = 0$ when $t = 0$ and that its velocity then is $(K/\alpha m)$. Solve for the position as a function of time, and express the force as a function of position. From this, obtain the potential corresponding to the force.
   Answer: $V(x) \propto x^2$.

2. Develop an expression for the work done by one gm-mole of an ideal gas in changing its volume under isothermal conditions.
   Answer: $RT \ln \dfrac{\overline{V}_f}{\overline{V}_i}$.

3. A 10.0-kg weight having an initial horizontal velocity of 1.00 m/sec impinges upon a piston and forces the latter to compress 1.00 gm-mole of ideal gas isothermally. Initially the gas was at STP. Assuming that no dissipation occurs and that the weight finally is brought to rest, determine the pressure thereupon developed in the gas. (Regard the entire motion as occurring parallel to the earth's surface so that gravitational effects may be disregarded.)
   Answer: 1.0022 atm.

4. Develop an expression for the work done by one gm-mole of a van der Waals gas in changing its volume under isothermal conditions.
   Answer: $RT \ln \dfrac{\overline{V}_f - b}{\overline{V}_i - b} + a\left(\dfrac{1}{\overline{V}_f} - \dfrac{1}{\overline{V}_i}\right)$.

5. By Eq. (2–12) the viscous force acting upon an object immersed in a fluid is proportional to the velocity gradient in its immediate vicinity. Under some conditions, we may suppose that the latter is proportional to the object's speed, measured relative to the fluid. Such conditions are implicit in *Stokes' equation* for the viscous force acting upon a sphere of a radius r and mass m moving with speed v_x relative to the stationary fluid which has a coefficient

of viscosity η:

$$f_x = -6\pi r\eta v_x.$$

Assume that initially ($t = 0$, $x = 0$) the sphere has the speed $v_x(0)$ and obtain its position as a function of time.

Answer: $x = \dfrac{mv_x(0)}{6\pi r\eta} (1 - e^{-6\pi r\eta t/m})$.

6. Establish that the viscous force given by Stokes' equation is not conservative (i.e., not derivable from a potential which depends upon position alone, and independent of initial conditions.)

7. Assuming the applicability of Stokes' equation, determine the maximum distance traversed by a particle having the following parameters:

$$W = 30 \text{ gm/gm-mole,} \qquad r = 2.0 \cdot 10^{-8} \text{ cm,}$$
$$v_x(0) = 4.5 \times 10^4 \text{ cm/sec,} \qquad \eta = 2.0 \times 10^{-4} \text{ poise.}$$

Answer: $3.0 \cdot 10^{-8}$ cm.

8. Extend the treatment in the text and show that the kinetic energy of three particles confined to motion in a straight line can be expressed as the sum of the kinetic energy of their center of mass and the kinetic energies of the three particles relative to their center of mass. [Extend Eq. (3–19).]

9. Show, for three particles confined to motion in a straight line and subject to pairwise interaction potentials, that the total energy relative to their center of mass is a constant of their motion. [Extend (Eq. (3–23).]

10. Consider two particles moving at right angles with respect to each other and which ultimately suffer a collision. Assuming point masses, verify that

$$\frac{T_a(f)}{T_b(f)} = \frac{1 + \dfrac{(m_a - m_b)^2}{4m_a m_b} \dfrac{T_a(i)}{T_b(i)}}{\dfrac{(m_a - m_b)^2}{4m_a m_b} + \dfrac{T_a(i)}{T_b(i)}}.$$

Determine a relationship between the masses that will always give final kinetic energies of the two particles which are equal regardless of their initial values. [Such is not possible for the situation described by Eq. (3–37).] *Answer:* $m_b/m_a = 3 \pm \sqrt{8}$.

11. Suppose that all the molecules in one cubic centimeter of an ideal gas of molecular weight 30 gm/gm-mole at STP are to have their speeds increased (in a random direction) by 1.00 m/sec. How much energy must be supplied? *Answer:* Approximately 1.31×10^{-4} cal.

12. The vapor pressure of graphite at 2330°C has been determined by an effusion method. By allowing the vapor to effuse into a vacuum, it was found that 0.185 mg of carbon escaped in an hour through an opening with an area of 3.25 mm². Using Eq. (3–66) with $\alpha = 0.921$ (as obtained in Chapter 4), estimate the vapor pressure of graphite. *Answer:* 3.98×10^{-4} mm Hg.

13. The vapor pressure of naphthalene ($W = 128.16$ gm/gm-mole) is 0.177 mm Hg at 30°C. Calculate the effusion rate from these data. (This approximates the maximum isothermal evaporation rate.)

    Answer: 6.74 gm/cm^2 · sec.

14. Assume that a gas at STP consists of 70.0 mole percent nitrogen and 30.0 mole percent oxygen. Under these conditions, a slow steady flow of the gas is maintained past one side of an orifice of area 4.25 mm^2. The other side of the orifice is kept at practically zero pressure. Estimate the composition of the effusing gas.

    Answer: 71.4 mole percent nitrogen.

15. A vessel contains an ideal gas at STP. Its exterior is kept at practically zero pressure. A small hole is punctured in the wall of the vessel, and gas begins to effuse. Assuming that the gas can be maintained at constant temperature in the vessel, obtain the differential equation for the pressure as a function of time:

$$\frac{dP}{dt} = -\left\{\frac{\alpha A}{4V} \sqrt{\frac{3RT}{W}}\right\} P,$$

where the symbols have their usual meaning.

4 · MOLECULAR DISTRIBUTIONS

1. PROBABILITY AND AVERAGES

The previous analysis we have undertaken has introduced the notion of *molecular averages* of the kinetic energy and speed. In the case of the former quantity, the detailed calculation of its value was avoided simply because of the identification we were able to make via the theoretical and experimental equations of state for an ideal gas. With regard to the average speed of a molecule, we did not fare so well, noting only that it differed slightly from the root-mean-square value. The latter is, of course, readily obtained from the average kinetic energy of a molecule. [We could exploit experimental values of effusion rates to evaluate the quantity α in Eq. (3–64), but the precision accompanying such data is not as great as that associated with the equation of state.] From a detailed knowledge of the values of $\rho(p_z)$ in Eq. (3–61), we can calculate the average speed. The present chapter is thus directed to such calculations.

Rather than deal immediately with molecular distributions, we shall first consider the mathematics of calculating averages in more general terms. This seems desirable in view of the widespread utilization of averaging procedures. For simplicity, we commence with quantities which are restricted to having possible values which are distinct and separate from one another. An illustration is the value of a coin of U.S. currency. A given coin may have the value (in cents): 1, 5, 10, 25, 50, 100. Given a handful of coins, we may wish to know the "average value" of one of the coins. This value depends, of course, upon what is meant by the phrase "average value." In the usual sense, we take it to mean the total value of the handful of coins divided by the number of coins. In mathematical terms, if y_k is the value of the kth coin and there are a total of N coins, the average or *mean* value of a coin is defined as

$$\bar{y} \equiv \sum_{k=1}^{N} y_k / N. \qquad (4\text{–}1)$$

If $n(y)$ is the *number* of coins in the handful *having the value* y, we can also write

$$\bar{y} \equiv \sum_{y=1,5,10,25,50,100} n(y)\, y / N, \qquad (4\text{–}2)$$

where

$$\sum_{y=1,5,10,25,50,100} n(y) = N. \qquad (4\text{–}3)$$

Alternatively, if fr (y) is the *fraction* of coins *having the value* y, we have

$$\text{fr}(y) \equiv \frac{n(y)}{N} \geq 0, \tag{4-4}$$

so that we can express the mean value as

$$\bar{y} \equiv \sum_{y=1,5,10,25,50,100} \text{fr}(y)\, y, \tag{4-5}$$

with

$$\sum_{y=1,5,10,25,50,100} \text{fr}(y) = 1. \tag{4-6}$$

The similarity of these expressions with those already employed is to be noted.

The function fr (y) is frequently referred to as a *probability distribution* function, suggested by the observation that the *probability* of selecting a coin of specified value from the handful is equal to the fraction of such coins. This is a useful concept only if the process of selection has no bias for coins of any specified denomination. We shall assume it to be so. In these terms, the *mean value* of a coin is identical with its *probable value*. (Not, however, its most probable value, as we shall see.) We shall retain the former terminology.

A knowledge of the values of fr (y) gives one a complete characterization of the handful of coins with regard to their values. Other averages can be computed. Thus,

$$\overline{y^2} = \sum_y \text{fr}(y)\, y^2, \tag{4-7}$$

$$\overline{y^3} = \sum_y \text{fr}(y)\, y^3, \quad \text{etc.}, \tag{4-8}$$

where the summation is carried out over the possible values of y. [The more explicit instructions of Eqs. (4–2) through (4–6) will be dropped, for the sake of simplicity in notation.] In the present illustration there are six values of y. Hence, if we are told the values of $\overline{y^n}$, $n = 0, 1, 2, 3, 4, 5$, there will be six linear equations in terms of which the six values of fr (y) can be evaluated. The quantity $\overline{y^n}$ is called the nth *moment* of y. In the present illustration, any six (independent) moments determine the distribution.

To illustrate simply the determination of the distribution, we may consider a case of two kinds of coins, say nickels and dimes. In this case the average value of a coin must have a value ranging between five and ten cents. A knowledge of the average value suffices to determine the distribution. To see this, we write

$$1 = \text{fr}(5) + \text{fr}(10) \quad \text{and} \quad \bar{y} = 5\,\text{fr}(5) + 10\,\text{fr}(10).$$

Hence, elimination of fr (5) yields

$$\bar{y} - 5 = 5\,f(10),$$

or

$$\text{fr}\,(10) = \frac{\bar{y}}{5} - 1$$

and

$$\text{fr}\,(5) = 2 - \frac{\bar{y}}{5}.$$

The identical mathematical procedure is involved in cases where y has more than two possible values.

In general, it can be shown that the values of the moments always determine the distribution uniquely. A special distribution is the *singular distribution* for which fr (y) has only one nonzero value; this nonzero value, by Eq. (4–6), can only be unity. The singular distribution thus has the property that

$$\overline{y^n} = (\bar{y})^n \qquad \text{for all } n.$$

For nonsingular distributions [i.e., more than one nonzero value of $f(y)$]

$$\overline{y^n} \neq (\bar{y})^n \qquad \text{for some } n.$$

In particular, we examine the quantity

$$\overline{y^2} - (\bar{y})^2 = \sum_y \text{fr}\,(y)[y^2 - (\bar{y})^2],$$

since $(\bar{y})^2$ is independent of y in the summation. Now we notice also that

$$(\bar{y})^2 = \bar{y} \sum_y \text{fr}\,(y)\, y,$$

so that we may write

$$(\bar{y})^2 = \sum_y \text{fr}\,(y)[2y\bar{y} - (\bar{y})^2].$$

Hence, we obtain the important result that

$$\overline{y^2} - (\bar{y})^2 = \sum_y \text{fr}\,(y)[y^2 - 2y\bar{y} + (\bar{y})^2] = \overline{(y - \bar{y})^2} \geq 0. \qquad (4\text{–}9)$$

The quantity $\overline{(y - \bar{y})^2}$ is the *dispersion* of the distribution. Since it is the average of only nonnegative quantities, it can vanish only if all but one value of fr (y) vanishes. Hence a zero value for the dispersion corresponds to a singular distribution. From Eq. (4–9) we note that α of Eq. (3–64) is a number less than unity.

The meaning of the average value of a function of y can be exhibited in terms of the moments. If the function can be expressed as a power series,

$$g(y) = \sum_{n=0}^{\infty} a_n y^n,$$

then we take

$$\overline{g(y)} \equiv \sum_{n=0}^{\infty} a_n \left[\sum_y \mathrm{fr}\,(y)\, y^n \right] = \sum_{n=0}^{\infty} a_n \overline{y^n}. \qquad (4\text{–}10)$$

As previously, nonsingular distributions usually yield

$$\overline{g(y)} \neq g(\bar{y}).$$

However, special cases can be constructed where the equality is satisfied.

Frequently, one needs to employ distributions which depend upon the values of more than a single variable. Such a case occurs if we wish to speak of the fraction of coins which are selected and exhibit a *head* or a *tail*. A certain distribution of coins will be obtained if the handful is placed upon a flat surface and the face in contact with the surface is recorded as the value of the property in question. The distribution we seek can be expressed through the function $\mathrm{fr}\,(y, s)$, where $s = h$ for *heads* and $s = t$ for *tails*. The quantity $\mathrm{fr}\,(y, s)$ is the *fraction* of coins *of value y which have the s-face* (in contact with the surface). Clearly,

$$\sum_{s=t,h} \mathrm{fr}\,(y, s) = \mathrm{fr}\,(y), \qquad (4\text{–}11\mathrm{a})$$

while

$$\sum_y \mathrm{fr}\,(y, s) = \mathrm{fr}\,(s) \qquad (4\text{–}11\mathrm{b})$$

is the fraction of all coins which have the s-face. This distribution function is referred to as a *joint distribution* function. Its utility may be illustrated by the following question. What is the average value of the coins which show tails? The answer to this question can be expressed simply, as

$$\overline{y_t} = \frac{\sum_y \mathrm{fr}\,(y, t)\, y}{\sum_y \mathrm{fr}\,(y, t)}. \qquad (4\text{–}12)$$

This result can be seen to correspond to averaging over the y-distribution of coins which show tails. [Compare with the equation following Eq. (3–47).]

In analogous terms, the average value of the coins which show heads is

$$\overline{y_h} = \frac{\sum_y \mathrm{fr}\,(y, h)\, y}{\sum_y \mathrm{fr}\,(y, h)}. \qquad (4\text{–}13)$$

Hence we can express the average value of y as

$$\bar{y} = \sum_{s=t,h} \text{fr}\,(s)\,\bar{y_s}. \tag{4–14}$$

A comparison of Eqs. (4–5) and (4–12) through (4–14) reveals the common feature that an average is a sum of terms of the same form: each term is the product of a value of some quantity and the probability (or fraction of objects) that corresponds to such a value. The exact details of averaging may vary, but the *form does not vary*.

The joint distribution, illustrated above, is a more elaborate quantity than the distribution function for a single property. Nevertheless, the procedure outlined for a determination of the distribution function from a knowledge of the mean values of various moments can be extended to the case of joint distributions. We shall not pursue the matter, however, leaving it to the interested student to investigate.

We shall confine our attention to joint distributions of a special sort which are pertinent to our interest in molecular averages. We begin with an examination of joint distributions of *statistically independent* properties. If x and y are two properties of an object in a collection, fr (x, y) is the fraction of objects having both the value x *and* the value y. In the general situation we may have the quantity

$$\text{fr}\,(x, y) \neq \text{fr}\,(x)\,\text{fr}\,(y).$$

When this relation is obeyed, the properties represented by x and y are said to be *statistically dependent*, or correlated. (In terms of the previous illustration, the property of showing a head and having a ten-cent value are independent properties *of a coin*. However, since they may be related *in the distribution* one qualifies this relation by the terminology given.) Joint distributions of properties which are statistically independent, or uncorrelated, satisfy the relation

$$\text{fr}\,(x, y) = \text{fr}\,(x)\,\text{fr}\,(y). \tag{4–15}$$

This statement corresponds to a prescription for calculating the probability of two independent events. It is evident that

$$\sum_x \text{fr}\,(x) = \sum_y \text{fr}\,(y) = 1. \tag{4–16}$$

In the previous example, Eq. (4–15) would correspond to a distribution in which the probability of finding a ten-cent coin, say, is independent of its being head or tails. Then Eqs. (4–12) through (4–14) would all have the same values. Statistical independence means that the properties are necessarily *unrelated*.

The distributions we shall work with have the additional property that for any *arbitrary* function $h(u)$,

$$\bar{h} = \sum_{x,y} h(x) \, \text{fr} \, (x, y) = \sum_{x} h(x) \, \text{fr} \, (x)$$

$$= \sum_{x,y} h(y) \, \text{fr} \, (x, y) = \sum_{y} h(y) \, \text{fr} \, (y). \qquad (4\text{--}17)$$

This equation corresponds to the assertion that the mean value of any function of the x-property is the same as the mean value of the *same* function of the y-property. Since the function is arbitrary, we can imagine it to be nonzero for only a specified value of its argument. Then we conclude:

(1) The possible values of x are identical with the possible values of y. Otherwise, a function could be chosen which would be zero for all y-values and nonzero for some x-value, and vice versa. This would contradict Eq. (4–17).

(2) The two distribution functions fr (x) and fr (y), apart from labels, must be identical. If otherwise, Eq. (4–17) would again be contradicted.

Joint distributions satisfying this property are said to be *symmetric* with respect to exchange of the variables. In mathematical terms, we characterize *statistically independent symmetric* distributions by the equation

$$\text{fr} \, (x, y) = \text{fr} \, (y, x) = \text{fr} \, (x) \, \text{fr} \, (y), \qquad (4\text{--}18)$$

with

$$\text{fr} \, (x = u) \equiv \text{fr} \, (y = u) = f(u). \qquad (4\text{--}19)$$

The stringent requirement of symmetry means that the physical properties upon which the distribution depends are *related* in some essential way.

The relations which have been described can be extended in two ways. First of all, they are immediately extended to include many variables. We shall not elaborate such extension here, but deal with it as the situations arise which necessitate doing so. The second extension involves dealing with variables which are not restricted to separate and distinct sets of values. These are variables which are termed *continuous variables*. To deal with these, we must make a transcription of the discrete formalism we have employed to one which is more natural for continuous variables. This is done conveniently by dealing with a variable whose values correspond to certain *ranges* of the values of a continuous variable.

To make the extension to continuous variables clear, we shall consider a more-or-less explicit example. Thus, we shall consider a collection of stones selected in an unprejudiced manner from a gravel pit. This collection consists of members differing in size, shape, weight, color, and a variety of other properties. Only the property of weight will be dealt with here.

The weight of a stone may be imagined to be unrestricted in value. Almost any weight is possible. To describe the distribution of the stones according to weight, it may suffice for some purposes that all stones having weights ranging from 0.00–0.99 gram be grouped together, all stones having weights ranging from 1.00–1.99 grams be grouped together, and so forth. The fraction of each group is easily computed and the set of fractions is a distribution function for the categories of weight ranges of the stones. Frequently, this sort of distribution function is represented by a *histogram*, as in Fig. 4–1. The height of each rectangle refers to the fraction of stones having weights falling within the ranges indicated by the base of the rectangle.

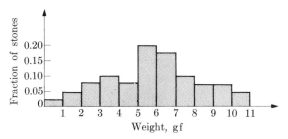

Fig. 4–1. Histogram.

In Fig. 4–1, we may verify that the distribution function has the following values:

$$\begin{aligned}
\text{fr}\,(x) &= 0.025, && 0 < x < 1 \\
&= 0.050, && 1 < x < 2 \\
&= 0.075, && 2 < x < 3 \\
&= 0.100, && 3 < x < 4 \\
&= 0.075, && 4 < x < 5, \text{ etc.}
\end{aligned}$$

Within the accuracy of the characterization of the collection afforded by the histogram, a typical value of weight for the members of each group may be taken as the middle of the range. These assigned values are not precise values of the average weight in each group, but will serve as a first guess to that value. With these values of weights, an average (approximate) value of a stone in the collection may be computed from the previously given expressions. The resulting value can be seen to differ from the "true" mean value by *at most* one-half gram.

This last remark follows immediately from the observation that the maximum weight of a stone in each group cannot exceed the upper limit of the range. Similarly, the minimum weight must not be less than the lower limit of the range.

If the mean weight is $\overline{m}$, then

$$\overline{m} \leq \overline{m_{\max}} = \sum_{k=1}^{12} k \ \text{fr} \ (k)$$

$$\geq \overline{m_{\min}} = \sum_{k=1}^{12} (k-1) \ \text{fr} \ (k) = \overline{m_{\max}} - 1.$$

However, the value we have considered is

$$\overline{m_{\text{approx}}} = \frac{\overline{m_{\max}} + \overline{m_{\min}}}{2} = \overline{m_{\max}} - \tfrac{1}{2} = \overline{m_{\min}} + \tfrac{1}{2}.$$

Therefore, using the above inequalities, we have

$$\overline{m_{\text{approx}}} - \tfrac{1}{2} \leq m \leq \overline{m_{\text{approx}}} + \tfrac{1}{2}.$$

Higher moments than the first, however, will have deviations from their "true" values possibly greater than one-half.

If a more precise value of the mean is desired, it is essential to have a more precise knowledge of the distribution. Thus, a smaller range of values for each interval of weights may be adopted and the corresponding frequency distribution determined. A new histogram can be prepared on this basis. What changes in Fig. 4–1 will result can be anticipated qualitatively as follows. Each interval has associated with it a definite fraction. If that interval is subdivided, it is apparent that the fraction associated with each subinterval will be less than that of the original interval. The sum of the fractions of each subinterval is just the original fraction. As the subdivisions become smaller and smaller, the corresponding fractions diminish. Ultimately, therefore, the histogram will be a horizontal curve of zero height.

This situation can be eliminated by constructing a histogram with a new ordinate, as follows. Instead of identifying the ordinate with the relevant fraction, we may choose to identify the *area of each rectangle with the fraction*. Thereupon, the ordinates do not necessarily vanish as the range of the subintervals diminish. In terms of an interval of size Δx, the ordinate will be designated by $\text{fr} \ (x)/\Delta x$. The corresponding quantity is referred to as a *fraction density, frequency density,* or *probability density*. Analogous to the histogram of Fig. 4–1, we can construct Fig. 4–2, in which the intervals have been halved. It has been constructed so that the total *area* of the subintervals sums to the *area* of the original intervals in Fig. 4–1.

In terms of an arbitrary set of ranges Δm_k, we can approximate the actual distribution at hand more closely if each Δm_k is made extremely small. The corresponding histogram will then have an outline like the smooth

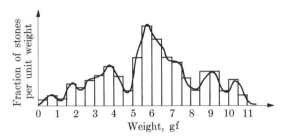

Fig. 4–2. Histogram and distribution density.

curve of Fig. 4–2. For any arbitrary set of ranges the mean value of the weight of a stone is approximately given by the usual form:

$$\overline{m_{\text{approx}}} = \sum_{k=1}^{N} m_k \, \text{fr} \, (m_k),$$

where m_k is a value of the weight lying in the range Δm_k (of which there are N) and fr (m_k) is the fraction of stones having weights in this range. In terms of the fraction density, we also have

$$\overline{m_{\text{approx}}} = \sum_{k=1}^{N} m_k \left(\frac{\text{fr} \, (m_k)}{\Delta m_k} \right) \Delta m_k. \tag{4–20}$$

Now, as each Δm_k is made smaller and smaller, we observe that the fraction density approaches a value

$$\lim_{\Delta m_k \to 0} \left(\frac{\text{fr} \, (m_k)}{\Delta m_k} \right) = \rho(m_k),$$

so that

$$\overline{m} = \lim_{\substack{\Delta m_k \to 0 \\ N \to \infty}} \sum_{k=1}^{N} m_k \left(\frac{\text{fr} \, (m_k)}{\Delta m_k} \right) \Delta m_k \equiv \int_0^\infty dm \{ m\rho(m) \}, \tag{4–21}$$

according to the definition of an integral as the limit of a sum. Of course, we have the condition that

$$\int_0^\infty dm \, \rho(m) = 1. \tag{4–22}$$

In terms of a continuous distribution, Eqs. (4–21) and (4–22) are the extensions of Eqs. (4–5) and (4–6). All the relations we have described for distributions in terms of discrete variables carry over for distribution densities in terms of continuous variables. They may be extended to the case of joint distribution functions as well. Some of the formal relations involved are summarized in Table 4–1. They all depend upon the realiza-

TABLE 4–1

RELATIONS BETWEEN DISCRETE AND CONTINUOUS DISTRIBUTIONS

Discrete	Continuous
fr (x)	$\rho(x)\,dx$
$\sum_x \{\cdots\}$ fr (x)	$\int dx\,\rho(x)\{\cdots\}$
fr (x, y, z)	$\rho(x, y, z)\,dx\,dy\,dz$
$\sum_x\sum_y\sum_z \{\cdots\}$ fr (x, y, z)	$\iiint dx\,dy\,dz\,\rho(x, y, z)\{\cdots\}$
fr (x, y) = fr (x) fr (y)	$\rho(x, y)\,dx\,dy = \rho_1(x)\rho_2(y)\,dx\,dy$
fr $(x = u)$ = fr $(y = u)$	$\rho(x = u)\,du = \rho(y = u)\,du$

tion that, for a continuous distribution,

Fraction of systems having values
$$\text{between } x \text{ and } x + dx = \rho(x)\,dx. \tag{4–23a}$$
Hence,

Fraction of systems having values
$$\text{between } x_1 \text{ and } x_2 = \int_{x_1}^{x_2} dx\,\rho(x). \tag{4–23b}$$

Thus, as originally introduced, the *area* under a portion of the $\rho(x)$ vs. x curve is equal to the fraction of systems having values of x lying between the extremes.

2. MAXWELL'S VELOCITY DISTRIBUTION

We now turn to the question raised earlier: what is the molecular distribution in momenta, i.e., the quantity we have represented earlier by $\rho(p_z)$? Immediately, we can take note of two things before attempting an answer: (1) the molecular distribution in *velocities* will be equally useful in a determination of molecular averages of functions of the momentum; (2) a distribution density will be more realistic to consider in the present case, for the obvious reason that velocities of molecules are not restricted to distinct, separate values. With this foresight, we can immediately deal with the velocity distribution as follows:

Fraction of molecules with velocities
$$\text{between } v_x \text{ and } v_x + dv_x,$$
$$v_y \text{ and } v_y + dv_y,$$
$$v_z \text{ and } v_z + dv_z = \rho(v_x, v_y, v_z)\,dv_x\,dv_y\,dv_z. \tag{4–24}$$

The function $\rho(v_x, v_y, v_z)$ is restricted by the assumptions we have made for ideal gases. From the behavior we have discerned for mass-points, we must insist that the distribution density is unaltered by interchanging the values of the velocity components. In mathematical terms this implies that

$$\rho(v_x, v_y, v_z) = \rho(v_y, v_x, v_z) = \rho(v_y, v_z, v_x), \text{ etc.}$$

The assumption of isotropy further requires that the distribution density be a function of the *speed* of a molecule. Otherwise, the likelihood of finding a molecule of specified speed will differ with the direction of motion and, hence, result in a lack of isotropy. For simplicity, we may express

$$\rho(v_x, v_y, v_z) = \rho(v_x^2 + v_y^2 + v_z^2).$$

This function is further restricted by the hypothesis that the components of velocity for mass-points are statistically independent. That is, the average properties of an ideal gas that depend only upon motion in the x-direction must be identical to the corresponding properties which depend upon motion in the y- or z-direction. (In the absence of such a restriction, the distribution function must be dependent upon direction. We shall consider this in the following section.) This requirement has the mathematical consequence that

$$\rho(v_x^2 + v_y^2 + v_z^2) = \rho(v_x^2)\rho(v_y^2)\rho(v_z^2), \tag{4–25}$$

where $\rho(u^2)$ on the right side of this equation is the *same function* of the indicated variable. Because of the meaning to be attached to $\rho(u^2)$, we must also require that

$$\int_{-\infty}^{+\infty} du\, \rho(u^2) = 1, \tag{4–26}$$

corresponding to the statement that the probability of finding a molecule with *some value* of a velocity component is unity.

To determine the consequences of Eq. (4–25), we consider the simpler mathematical problem expressed by

$$g(x + y) = f(x)f(y).$$

Here, g and f refer to continuous functions of the indicated variables. We can obtain the following relations:

$$\left[\frac{\partial g(x + y)}{\partial x}\right]_y = g'(x + y) = f'(x)f(y),$$

and

$$\left[\frac{\partial g(x + y)}{\partial y}\right]_x = g'(x + y) = f(x)f'(y),$$

the prime denoting the total derivative: $f'(u) = df(u)/du$. Thus we have

$$f'(x)f(y) = f(x)f'(y),$$

or

$$\left[\frac{f'(x)}{f(x)}\right] = \left[\frac{f'(y)}{f(y)}\right].$$

This equation reads: a certain function of x *alone* is equal to the same function of y *alone*. It can be consistent only if both functions are actually independent of the indicated variables. This, then, gives rise to the differential equation

$$\frac{f'(x)}{f(x)} = -b, \text{ independent of } x \text{ (or } y\text{)}.$$

This equation has the solution

$$f(x) = ae^{-bx}.$$

Hence we obtain

$$\rho(v_z^2) = ae^{-bv_z^2}.$$

In order to satisfy Eq. (4–26), b must be a positive number; otherwise the integral diverges. (Our previous choice of sign was made with this anticipation.) Then we have

$$a\int_{-\infty}^{+\infty} du\, e^{-bu^2} = 1.$$

Since

$$\int_{-\infty}^{+\infty} du\, e^{-bu^2} = \frac{1}{\sqrt{b}}\int_{-\infty}^{+\infty} d(\sqrt{b}\,u)e^{-(\sqrt{b}\,u)^2} = \frac{\sqrt{\pi}}{\sqrt{b}}, \qquad (4\text{–}27)$$

from known values of the integral, we have that

$$a = \sqrt{b/\pi}.$$

As a consequence,

$$\rho(v_z^2) = \sqrt{b/\pi}\, e^{-bv_z^2}. \qquad (4\text{–}28)$$

As it stands, the distribution density $\rho(v_z^2)$ contains a constant whose value appears to be arbitrary. However, the value of this constant determines the properties of an ideal gas, since changes in the molecular distribution of velocities are reflected in changes in the gaseous properties. In particular, one such property is the mean-square speed. We have seen that the kinetic-molecular theory of an ideal gas requires, by Eqs. (3–49), (3–52), and (3–53), that

$$\frac{1}{2m}\overline{p_z^2} = \frac{m}{2}\overline{v_z^2} = \frac{\bar{\epsilon}}{3} = \frac{kT}{2}.$$

But, in terms of the distribution in v_z, we have

$$\overline{v_z^2} = \sqrt{b/\pi} \int_{-\infty}^{+\infty} dv_z \, v_z^2 e^{-bv_z^2}.$$

By replacing the variable

$$\sqrt{b} \, v_z = u, \qquad \sqrt{b} \, dv_z = du,$$

it follows that

$$\overline{v_z^2} = \frac{1}{b\sqrt{\pi}} \int_{-\infty}^{+\infty} du \, u^2 e^{-u^2}.$$

The value of the integral can be looked up, but we can indicate a way to obtain it from a known integral. Notice that

$$J_c \equiv \int_{-\infty}^{+\infty} du \, u^2 e^{-cu^2} = -\frac{\partial}{\partial c} \int_{-\infty}^{+\infty} du \, e^{-cu^2} = -\frac{\partial}{\partial c} \left(\frac{\pi}{c}\right)^{1/2},$$

from Eq. (4–27). Hence the integral we want is

$$\lim_{c \to 1} J_c = \lim_{c \to 1} \frac{\pi^{1/2}}{2c^{3/2}} = \frac{\pi^{1/2}}{2}.$$

Thus we obtain

$$\frac{kT}{m} = \overline{v_z^2} = \frac{1}{2b},$$

or

$$b = \frac{m}{2kT} = \frac{W}{2RT}. \tag{4–29}$$

With this result, the distribution density reduces to

$$\rho(v_z^2) = \left(\frac{m}{2\pi kT}\right)^{1/2} \exp\left(-\frac{mv_z^2}{2kT}\right), \tag{4–30}$$

and

$$\rho(v_x^2 + v_y^2 + v_z^2) = \left(\frac{m}{2\pi kT}\right)^{3/2} \exp\left[-\frac{m(v_x^2 + v_y^2 + v_z^2)}{2kT}\right], \tag{4–31a}$$

$$= \left(\frac{m}{2\pi kT}\right)^{3/2} \exp\left[-\frac{(p_x^2 + p_y^2 + p_z^2)}{2mkT}\right]. \tag{4–31b}$$

The distribution density expressed in Eqs. (4–31) is known as *Maxwell's velocity distribution* (density) function. It enables us to evaluate all properties of an ideal gas which depend upon the molecular averages of functions of their velocities. Hence we now are in a position to evaluate the mean

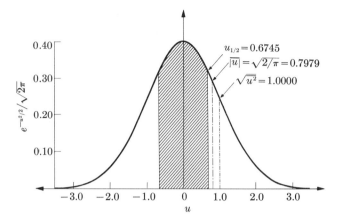

Fig. 4–3. The normal error curve.

speed of a molecule and, thus, α of Eq. (3–64). Before turning to this program, however, we shall examine briefly certain features of the velocity distribution.

The velocity distribution can be transformed into a form which is universal if velocity components are measured in units of the root mean square of the component velocity. That is, if we define the *dimensionless velocity*,

$$u_z = \left(\frac{m}{kT}\right)^{1/2} v_z, \tag{4–32}$$

then

$$\rho(v_z^2)\, dv_z = \frac{1}{\sqrt{2\pi}}\, e^{-u_z^2/2}\, du_z. \tag{4–33}$$

The function $(1/\sqrt{2\pi})e^{-u^2/2}$ is given in Fig. 4–3. It is referred to as the *normal error curve*. The area under the curve is unity. The cross-hatched area, corresponding to $|u| \leq 0.6745$, is one-half. This means that one-half the molecules have velocity components in a specified direction which range from -0.6745 to $+0.6745$ [in units of $(kT/m)^{1/2}$]. The value $u_{1/2} = 0.6745$ is termed the *median* speed. For comparison, the root-mean-square value, in these units, is unity. The fraction of molecules having velocity components in a specified direction less in magnitude than the root-mean-square value is 0.6825. Because the unit of velocity is $(kT/m)^{1/2}$, the velocity distribution in conventional units is broader for larger temperatures and narrower for smaller ones.

The mean value of the magnitude of a velocity component in a specified direction is easily computed. We have

$$\overline{|u_z|} = \frac{1}{\sqrt{2\pi}} \int_{-\infty}^{+\infty} du_z |u_z| e^{-u_z^2/2} = \frac{1}{\sqrt{2\pi}} \cdot 2 \int_0^{\infty} du_z |u_z| e^{-u_z^2/2},$$

because the integrand of the first integral is unaltered by a change in sign of u_z. The last integral is easily evaluated:

$$\int_0^\infty du_z u_z e^{-u_z^2/2} = \int_0^\infty d\left(\frac{u_z^2}{2}\right) e^{-u_z^2/2}$$

$$= -e^{-u_z^2/2}\Big|_0^\infty = 1.$$

Hence

$$\overline{|u_z|} = \sqrt{\frac{2}{\pi}} = 0.79789$$

and

$$\overline{|v_z|} = \left(\frac{kT}{m}\right)^{1/2} \overline{|u_z|} = \left(\frac{2kT}{\pi m}\right)^{1/2}.$$

From Eqs. (3–61) and (3–63), we obtain

$$\bar{\nu} = \tfrac{1}{2}\rho \left(\frac{2kT}{\pi m}\right)^{1/2} = \tfrac{1}{4}\rho\bar{S},$$

so that

$$\bar{S} = \left(\frac{8kT}{\pi m}\right)^{1/2}. \tag{4–34}$$

Hence, making the comparison with Eq. (3–64), we obtain

$$\alpha = \frac{\bar{S}}{\sqrt{\bar{S^2}}} = \left(\frac{8}{3\pi}\right)^{1/2} = 0.921.$$

We shall later confirm by a direct calculation of the average speed (in three dimensions) that Eq. (4–34) is obtained. For the moment, however, we note that our original task of determining the collision frequency of an ideal gas with the container walls is complete.

To obtain some appreciation of the joint distribution expressed by Maxwell's distribution formula, Eq. (4–31a), we restrict our attention to a two-dimensional velocity distribution. Defining

$$v_x = \left(\frac{kT}{m}\right)^{1/2} u_x,$$

and

$$v_y = \left(\frac{kT}{m}\right)^{1/2} u_y,$$

we have

$$\rho(v_x^2 + v_y^2)\, dv_x\, dv_y = \frac{1}{2\pi} \exp\left[-(u_x^2 + u_y^2)/2\right] du_x\, du_y.$$

The function $(1/2\pi) \exp\left[-(u_x^2 + u_y^2)/2\right]$ is indicated in Fig. 4–4. The region for which $u = \sqrt{u_x^2 + u_y^2} \leq 1.178$, as indicated in the diagram,

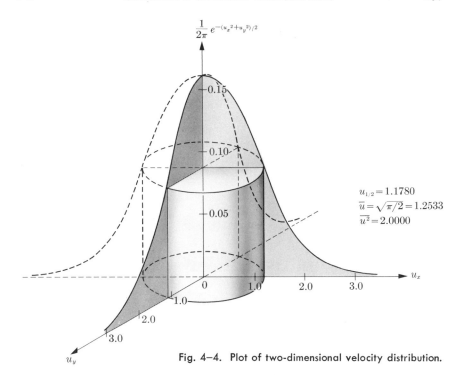

Fig. 4–4. Plot of two-dimensional velocity distribution.

has a volume of one-half, while the total volume under the distribution density function is unity. Half the molecules have two-dimensional speeds less than this value. The median two-dimensional speed is 1.178.

The average two-dimensional speed is easily computed by means of the *distribution-in-speeds*. From Fig. 4–5, we see that in terms of *polar coordinates* we have

$$u_x = u \cos \theta, \qquad u_y = u \sin \theta.$$

An integration over u_x and u_y is equivalent to an integration over u and θ. To accomplish a transformation of the integrals we need to determine the differential element of area. This is also indicated in Fig. 4–5. In effect, we have

$$\int_{-\infty}^{+\infty} du_x \int_{-\infty}^{+\infty} du_y \{\cdots\}$$

$$\equiv \int_0^\infty du \int_0^{2\pi} d\theta \, u \{\cdots\}.$$

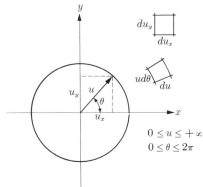

Fig. 4–5. Planar polar coordinate relations.

This means an equivalence between

$$\frac{1}{2\pi} \exp\left[-(u_x^2 + u_y^2)/2\right] du_x\, dy_x \quad \text{and} \quad \frac{1}{2\pi} e^{-u^2/2}\, u\, du\, d\theta.$$

The function

$$\frac{u}{2\pi} e^{-u^2/2} = \rho(u,\, \theta) \tag{4–35}$$

is the two-dimensional distribution density in terms of *speed* and *direction*. The distribution-in-speeds is found by integrating over all directions, and yields the function $ue^{-u^2/2}$. The average (two-dimensional) speed is given by

$$\bar{u} = \int_0^\infty du\, u^2 e^{-u^2/2}$$

$$= \sqrt{\pi/2} = 1.2533.$$

The root-mean-square (two-dimensional) speed is

$$\overline{u^2} = \int_0^\infty du\, u^3 e^{-u^2/2}$$

$$= \lim_{c \to 1/2} \left\{-\frac{\partial}{\partial c} \int_0^\infty du\, u e^{-cu^2}\right\}$$

$$= \lim_{c \to 1/2} \left\{-\frac{\partial}{\partial c} \frac{1}{2c} \int_0^\infty d(cu^2) e^{-cu^2}\right\}$$

$$= \lim_{c \to 1/2} \frac{1}{2c^2} = 2.$$

Hence, $\sqrt{\overline{u^2}} = \sqrt{2} = 1.4142.$

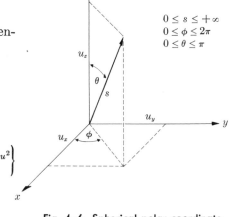

$$0 \le s \le +\infty$$
$$0 \le \phi \le 2\pi$$
$$0 \le \theta \le \pi$$

Fig. 4–6. Spherical polar coordinate relations.

The comparable distribution-in-speeds in three dimensions is obtained by expressing the velocity components in terms of spherical polar coordinates. This is indicated in Fig. 4–6. It is seen that

$$u_z = s \cos\theta,$$
$$u_y = s \sin\theta \sin\phi,$$
$$u_x = s \sin\theta \cos\phi.$$

It can be shown that, as previously, an integration over the components of velocity is equivalent to an integration over the polar coordinates $(s,\, \theta,\, \phi)$. Furthermore, one finds that

$$\int_{-\infty}^{+\infty} du_x \int_{-\infty}^{+\infty} du_y \int_{-\infty}^{+\infty} du_z\{\cdots\} = \int_0^{2\pi} d\phi \int_0^\pi d\theta \sin\theta \int_0^\infty ds\, s^2\{\cdots\}.$$

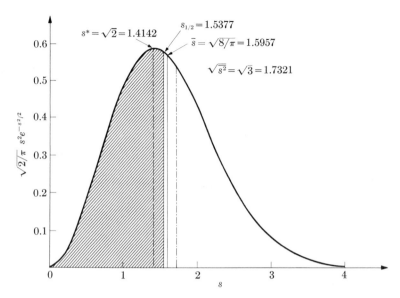

Fig. 4–7. Plot of distribution-in-speeds.

Hence, we obtain the three-dimensional distribution density in terms of speed and direction as

$$\rho(s, \theta, \phi) = \frac{1}{(2\pi)^{3/2}} s^2 \sin\theta e^{-s^2/2}. \tag{4-36}$$

The distribution-in-speeds is found by integrating over θ and ϕ, and yields the function

$$\rho(s) = \sqrt{2/\pi}\, s^2 e^{-s^2/2}. \tag{4-37}$$

This function is plotted in Fig. 4–7. The following quantities are easily obtained:

Most probable speed,	$s^* = \sqrt{2}$	$= 1.4142$	
Median speed,	$s_{1/2} = 1.5377$		
Average speed,	$\bar{s} = \sqrt{8/\pi}$	$= 1.5957$	
Root-mean-square speed,	$\sqrt{\bar{s^2}} = \sqrt{3}$	$= 1.7321.$	

The distribution-in-speeds leads simply to the distribution-in-energy. The latter is sometimes preferred for some calculations. If we relate the kinetic energy to its speed, we have

$$\epsilon = \frac{m}{2}(v_x^2 + v_y^2 + v_z^2) = \frac{m}{2}\left(\frac{kT}{m}\right)s^2 = \frac{kT}{2}s^2.$$

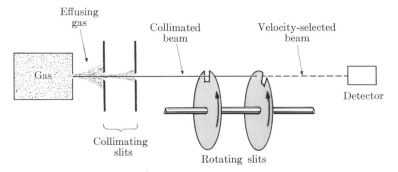

Fig. 4–8. Schematics of molecular beam with velocity selection.

Hence

$$ds = \frac{1}{2}\left(\frac{2}{kT}\right)^{1/2} \epsilon^{-1/2}\, d\epsilon$$

and, by Eq. (4–37),

$$\rho(s)\, ds = \rho(\epsilon)\, d\epsilon = \frac{1}{\sqrt{2\pi}}\left(\frac{2}{kT}\right)^{3/2} \epsilon^{1/2} e^{-\epsilon/kT}\, d\epsilon. \tag{4–38}$$

This distribution enables one to calculate the most probable energy, the median energy, etc.

The original program of determining the molecular distribution of velocities, in order to evaluate the average speed of a molecule of an ideal gas, now has been completed. The resulting distribution, however, is no mathematical artifact. It asserts something about the molecular nature of gases under conditions of very low pressures. Consequently, we are led to inquire whether the distribution of velocities is capable of direct experimental verification. As reasonable as the derivations have been, only the test of experiment can decide a question of physical correctness. This question has received a great deal of attention, especially in the past forty years.

The *molecular beam* has become an increasingly important chemical tool in recent years. In schematic terms, indicated in Fig. 4–8, a low-pressure gas is allowed to effuse through a set of small openings which collimates the beam. The collimated beam of molecules is passed between rotating shutters, the rotational speed of which allows passage of only those molecules which have the requisite velocity. A change in the rotational speed permits selection of other molecules in the effusing, collimated beam, with a different requisite velocity. The velocity-selected beam is allowed to impinge upon a detecting device which measures the number of molecules reaching it per unit time.

To relate the theoretical distribution to the experiment, we must utilize the former to yield a quantity which is to be measured. In the present experiment, we must determine the number of molecules of each range of speeds which will reach the detector. Such molecules must have velocity components normal to the beam which are relatively small. Those with appreciable lateral velocities will be eliminated by the slits. The number of molecules which pass through the final collimating slit per unit time depends upon the area of the slit. If the latter is extremely small, the collimated beam will be comprised of only those molecules which have a direction of the beam itself. Since the rate at which such molecules pass through the slit is limited by their effusion rate, and the latter is proportional to their speed (as dealt with in the previous chapter), the *distribution of speeds in the collimated beam* is determined by [note the difference from Eq. (4–37)]

$$f(s) = \tfrac{1}{2}s^3 e^{-s^2/2}, \tag{4–39}$$

with

$$\int_0^\infty ds\, f(s) = 1.$$

In order to relate Eq. (4–39) to the measurements, we must analyze the effect of the rotating slits. They may be assumed to rotate at a fixed angular speed ω, with a fixed angular displacement ϕ_0 of the slots. As a result, there is a time interval between the instants at which the first and second rotating slits permit passage of the molecular beam. Only molecules possessing a speed just sufficient to traverse the distance between the slits should reach the detector. However, because the slits have a macroscopic size, there will be a range of speeds associated with the molecules which reach the detector. The relations involved can be made clear from Fig. 4–9. The minimum time interval of passage for a molecule is

$$t_{\min} = \frac{\phi_{\min}}{\omega}.$$

The maximum time interval is

$$t_{\max} = \frac{\phi_{\max}}{\omega}.$$

With a distance l between the rotating slits, the corresponding speeds of molecules that may reach the detector are

$$s_{\max} = \frac{l\omega}{\phi_{\min}}$$

and

$$s_{\min} = \frac{l\omega}{\phi_{\max}}.$$

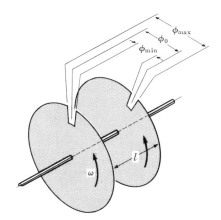

Fig. 4–9. Relations in rotating slits for beam velocity selector.

Since the discs are rotating at fixed angular speed, the median speed of traversable molecules is

$$s_0 = \frac{l\omega}{\phi_0} = \frac{l\omega}{(\phi_{\min} + \phi_{\max})/2}. \tag{4–40a}$$

Therefore,

$$s_{\max} = s_0\left(\frac{\phi_{\min} + \phi_{\max}}{2\phi_{\min}}\right) \tag{4–40b}$$

and

$$s_{\min} = s_0\left(\frac{\phi_{\min} + \phi_{\max}}{2\phi_{\max}}\right). \tag{4–40c}$$

As a consequence of the selection performed by the rotating slits, we see that the average number of molecules reaching the detector per unit time is

$$I(s_0) = \tfrac{1}{2}C\int_{s_{\min}}^{s_{\max}} ds\, s^3 e^{-s^2/2}.$$

The quantity C is a constant which depends upon the actual sizes of the rotating slits, but which is independent of the angular speed. In any actual design, the slits are very small, so that $s_{\max}$ and $s_{\min}$ are very close in value. Then the integral (which can be evaluated exactly, however) can be expressed to good approximation as

$$I(s_0) \doteq \left[\frac{1}{4}\left(\frac{\phi_{\max}^2 - \phi_{\min}^2}{\phi_{\max}\phi_{\min}}\right)C\right]s_0^4 e^{-s_0^2/2},$$

where Eqs. (4–40) have been employed. In applying this equation to the

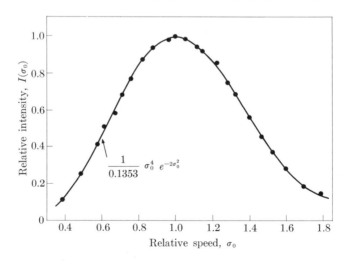

Fig. 4–10. Test of speed distribution. [Data on thallium vapor at 870°K. From Miller and Kusch, *Phys. Rev.* **99**, 1314 (1955).]

experimental data, it is convenient to measure speeds relative to the value for which $I(s_0)$ is a maximum. This value occurs for $s_0^* = 2$ [in our usual units of $(kT/m)^{1/2}$]. In these units, we have

$$I(\sigma_0) \propto \sigma_0^4 e^{-2\sigma_0^2}, \tag{4-41}$$

with

$$\sigma_0 = \frac{s_0}{s_0^*}.$$

Equation (4–41) is plotted in Fig. 4–10, and compared with data obtained for thallium vapor. The good agreement can be regarded as a significant test of the theory.

3. THE MAXWELL–BOLTZMANN DISTRIBUTION

It has been noted in Chapter 2 that nonuniform states of a gas are possible which are, nevertheless, equilibrium conditions of the gas. To prevent the flow of heat in such cases, the temperature of the gas must be uniform throughout its extent. But what about its density and composition? Need these properties also be uniform in the absence of transport of matter? Experimentally, the answer is in the negative.

To relate this state of affairs to the behavior of nonuniform ideal gases, we shall assume that the entire gas is subjected to an external force which may vary from point to point in the region occupied by it. In molecular terms, this means that the molecules of the ideal gas are subjected to forces which depend only upon their location in the gas. As we have seen in Chapter 3, this means that the momentum of a specified molecule will vary as it passes from one region to another. If our attention is restricted to (external) conservative forces, we can relate the momenta of the molecule in different regions to the potential energy in those regions. We have, as an obvious extension of Eq. (3–10),

$$\frac{p^2(1)}{2m} + \mathcal{V}(1) = \frac{p^2(2)}{2m} + \mathcal{V}(2), \tag{4-42}$$

where 1, 2 refer to two different regions, $\mathcal{V}$ is the potential energy function for the particle, and $p^2/2m$ is its total kinetic energy. This relation must hold for all molecules which are capable of passing from region (1) to region (2), and vice versa. Ultimately, all regions of the ideal gas may be assumed to be accessible to all of its molecules.

Now in any sufficiently small region of space we may assume that the gas is isotropic, so that our previous analysis is entirely applicable. In particular, the Maxwell distribution of velocities pertains. Hence, if we consider a number of molecules dn in the volume element $dx\, dy\, dz$ which have specified ranges of velocity components, we have

$$dn = \left(\frac{n}{V}\right)_1 \left(\frac{m}{2\pi kT}\right)^{3/2} e^{-p^2(1)/2kT} \, dv_x \, dv_y \, dv_z \, dx \, dy \, dz.$$

Here, $(n/V)_1$ is the density of molecules in region 1. These same molecules will ultimately find themselves in region 2, so we must have

$$dn = \left(\frac{n}{V}\right)_2 \left(\frac{m}{2\pi kT}\right)^{3/2} e^{-p^2(2)/2kT} \, dv_x \, dv_y \, dv_z \, dx \, dy \, dz.$$

But then, by Eq. (4–42), it follows that

$$\left(\frac{n}{V}\right)_2 = \left(\frac{n}{V}\right)_1 \exp\left(-\frac{[\mathcal{U}(2) - \mathcal{U}(1)]}{kT}\right), \tag{4–43}$$

the celebrated *Boltzmann distribution* formula, which relates the particle density in different regions of an isothermal ideal gas to the potential energies of these regions.

Equation (4–43) derives from the implicit assumption that $(dv_x \, dv_y \, dv_z \, dx \, dy \, dz)$ has identically the same value in the two regions considered. Having chosen its value in the first region, it is not possible to choose its value independently in the second. Nevertheless, it has the same value, as a consequence of the equations of motion of the particles. This statement is a simple version of *Liouville's Theorem* of the conservation of phase volume: $(dp_x \, dp_y \, dp_z \, dx \, dy \, dz)$.

We can incorporate Eqs. (4–31) and (4–43) to give the general *Maxwell-Boltzmann Distribution Law:*

$$dn = \left(\frac{n}{V}\right)_0 \left(\frac{m}{2\pi kT}\right)^{3/2} \exp\left(-\frac{[(p^2/2m) + \mathcal{U}]}{kT}\right) dv_x \, dv_y \, dv_z \, dx \, dy \, dz, \tag{4–44}$$

corresponding to the number of molecules of an ideal gas with velocities between (v_x, v_y, v_z) and $(v_x + dv_x, v_y + dv_y, v_z + dv_z)$ and positions between (x, y, z) and $(x + dx, y + dy, z + dz)$. While $\mathcal{U}$ usually depends upon position, the density of particles, $(n/V)_0$, refers to the position at which the potential $\mathcal{U}$ is taken to have zero value. In terms of Eq. (4–44), the total value of any molecular property which depends upon molecular velocity and position may be determined; its average value is determined by dividing by n. (That is, the Maxwell-Boltzmann distribution we have exhibited does not integrate to unity, as in the case of the Maxwell distribution.)

A particular case of some interest occurs when $\mathcal{U}$ is the potential energy of a molecule in a uniform gravitational field. Then

$$\mathcal{U} = mgh, \tag{4–45}$$

where $g = 980.665$ dynes/gm, is the acceleration due to the earth's gravity and h is the height above ground level, i.e., υ at the surface of the earth is taken to be zero. Since

$$\frac{n}{V} = \frac{P}{kT},$$

we obtain

$$P(h) = P(0)e^{-(Wg/RT)h}, \tag{4–46}$$

the so-called *barometric formula*. The difficulties associated with testing this expression in the earth's atmosphere are related to the lack of a truly uniform temperature. However, the variation with altitude is generally in accord with this expression, as indicated in Fig. 4–11.

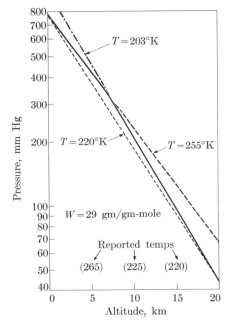

The Boltzmann distribution is derivable on more general thermodynamic grounds and so is not limited, by our analysis, to ideal gases. Indeed, by modifying Eq. (4–45) to refer to particles in a liquid, *viz.*,

$$\upsilon = \frac{m}{d_m}(d_m - d_l)gh,$$

which corrects for the buoyancy of the liquid (d_m being the density of the particle and d_l the density of the liquid), the number of particles per unit volume is given by Eq. (4–43). This equation was used by Perrin to obtain a value of Boltzmann's constant. Because R is known accurately, Eq. (3–53) permits Avogadro's number to be calculated. Perrin, using uniform particles of gamboge, found a value of 6.8×10^{23} for N_0, in good agreement with the currently best value of 6.0228×10^{23}.

Fig. 4–11. Variation of atmospheric pressure with altitude. [Data from *Handbook of Chemistry and Physics.*]

In concluding this section, we shall do so by noting that Eq. (4–46) depends upon the molecular weight of the gas. Consequently, a change in composition is expected for a gas mixture in a gravitational field. This same behavior may be expected in liquids, as indicated above, and is of great utility in separating colloidal solutions in a centrifuge, which increases the value of g enormously. (In this case, however, the potential is not a linear function of distance.)

4. MULTIPLE MOLECULAR DISTRIBUTIONS IN IDEAL GASES

The Maxwell-Boltzmann distribution, expressed in Eq. (4–44), permits one to calculate any average property of an ideal gas which can be said to depend only upon the velocities and positions of the *individual* molecules. It fails, however, to be of direct use for calculating averages of properties which depend, say, upon differences in the velocities of molecules. That is, if a property $g(x, y, z, v_x, v_y, v_z)$ is associated with a molecule of the indicated position and velocity components, the average value of such a property for all the molecules of an ideal gas is readily determined by the procedures discussed previously. The procedure is unspecified for evaluating the average value, say, of the relative speed between a pair of particles. In the present case, the function to be averaged is

$$v^{(\mathrm{rel})} = \sqrt{\{v_x^{(1)} - v_x^{(2)}\}^2 + \{v_y^{(1)} - v_y^{(2)}\}^2 + \{v_z^{(1)} - v_z^{(2)}\}^2},$$

which requires some extension of our previous prescriptions.

For an ideal gas, the motion of each individual molecule is evidently independent of the motion of any other. Since there is no interaction postulated between these molecules, no means exists of correlating their motions. Hence, if we suppose that there exists a *pairwise* distribution-in-velocities, it must have a density

$$\rho_2(v_x^{(1)}, v_y^{(1)}, v_z^{(1)}, v_x^{(2)}, v_y^{(2)}, v_z^{(2)}) = \rho(v_x^{(1)}, v_y^{(1)}, v_z^{(1)})\rho(v_x^{(2)}, v_y^{(2)}, v_z^{(2)}). \quad (4\text{–}47)$$

This equation follows immediately from the general properties of a joint distribution of statistically independent variables. [See Eq. (4–18).] The two ρ's, of course, are given by the original Maxwell distribution, Eq. (4–31a). Hence, considering two different types of molecules, we have (in vector notation)

$$\rho_2(\mathbf{v}^{(1)}, \mathbf{v}^{(2)})$$
$$= \left(\frac{m_1}{2\pi kT}\right)^{3/2} \left(\frac{m_2}{2\pi kT}\right)^{3/2} \exp\left(-\frac{m_1\{\mathbf{v}^{(1)}\}^2}{2kT}\right) \exp\left(-\frac{m_2\{\mathbf{v}^{(2)}\}^2}{2kT}\right).$$
$$(4\text{–}48)$$

The extension to any number of molecules is virtually immediate, since, regardless of the number, the velocities of the molecules are statistically independent. Thus we may write in such a case

$$\rho_n(\mathbf{v}^{(1)}, \mathbf{v}^{(2)}, \ldots, \mathbf{v}^{(n)}) = \prod_{k=1}^{n} \rho(\mathbf{v}^{(k)}), \quad (4\text{–}49)$$

where $\rho(\mathbf{v}^{(k)})$ is given by Eq. (4–31a).

The average value of any arbitrary function of the velocities of the molecules, $g(\mathbf{v}^{(1)}, \mathbf{v}^{(2)}, \ldots, \mathbf{v}^{(n)})$, can be expressed as

$$\bar{g} = \int_{-\infty}^{+\infty} \cdots \int g(\mathbf{v}^{(1)}, \mathbf{v}^{(2)}, \ldots, \mathbf{v}^{(n)}) \prod_{k=1}^{n} \left(\frac{m_k}{2\pi kT}\right)^{3/2}$$

$$\times \exp\left(-\frac{m_k \{\mathbf{v}^{(k)}\}^2}{2kT}\right) dv_x^{(k)} \, dv_y^{(k)} \, dv_z^{(k)}. \quad (4\text{–}50)$$

A special case concerns the average relative speed of a pair of molecules. Here the integration over all but two of the velocities (i.e., six velocity components) can be carried out, with the result that

$$\overline{v^{(\text{rel})}} = \left(\frac{m}{2\pi kT}\right)^3 \int_{-\infty}^{+\infty} \cdots \int dv_x^{(1)} \, dv_y^{(1)} \, dv_z^{(1)} \, dv_x^{(2)} \, dv_y^{(2)} \, dv_z^{(2)}$$

$$\times \sqrt{\{\mathbf{v}^{(1)} - \mathbf{v}^{(2)}\}^2} \exp\left(-\frac{m}{2kT}[\{\mathbf{v}^{(1)}\}^2 + \{\mathbf{v}^{(2)}\}^2]\right).$$

For simplicity, we have taken equal masses of the molecules. Now this cumbersome integral can be simplified considerably if we take advantage of the fact that the motion separates naturally into that of the center of mass of the pair and that of motion relative to the center of mass. [See Eq. (3–16).] Then,

$$\frac{m}{2}[\{\mathbf{v}^{(1)}\}^2 + \{\mathbf{v}^{(2)}\}^2] = m\left\{\frac{\mathbf{v}^{(1)} + \mathbf{v}^{(2)}}{2}\right\}^2 + \frac{m}{4}\{\mathbf{v}^{(1)} - \mathbf{v}^{(2)}\}^2.$$

The first term on the right side is the kinetic energy of the center of mass (i.e., a particle of mass $2m$). The second term is that of relative motion. If we define

$$\frac{\mathbf{v}^{(1)} + \mathbf{v}^{(2)}}{2} \equiv \mathbf{v}^{(12)}$$

and

$$\mathbf{v}^{(1)} - \mathbf{v}^{(2)} \equiv \mathbf{v}^{(\text{rel})},$$

it is demonstrable that

$$dv_x^{(1)} \, dv_y^{(1)} \, dv_z^{(1)} \, dv_x^{(2)} \, dv_y^{(2)} \, dv_z^{(2)} = dv_x^{(12)} \, dv_y^{(12)} \, dv_z^{(12)} \, dv_x^{(\text{rel})} \, dv_y^{(\text{rel})} \, dv_z^{(\text{rel})}.$$

This relation between volume elements in terms of which integration is to be carried out is the result of general mathematical methods. However, in an intuitive manner we may note that when velocity components are combined linearly, as we have done, the resulting velocities are equally valid as integrating variables. Any numerical factor which may be omitted by simply writing down these variables may be recovered by requiring that the over-all integration of Eq. (4–48) must be unity.

In mathematical terms, the transformation of volume elements involves the use of *Jacobians*, which is illustrated here. Suppose that x and y are two independent variables and that there are two others, $u = u(x, y)$ and $v = v(x, y)$. It is demonstrable that integration with respect to x and y can be carried out instead with respect to u and v. For that purpose it is sufficient to write

$$dx\, dy = |J(x, y \mid u, v)|\, du\, dv,$$

where

$$J(x, y \mid u, v) \equiv \begin{vmatrix} \left(\dfrac{\partial x}{\partial u}\right)_v & \left(\dfrac{\partial x}{\partial v}\right)_u \\[2mm] \left(\dfrac{\partial y}{\partial u}\right)_v & \left(\dfrac{\partial y}{\partial v}\right)_u \end{vmatrix}$$

is termed the Jacobian of the transformation from (x, y) to (u, v). Only the magnitude of the Jacobian is involved in the integration, and its evaluation is sometimes simplified by use of the identity

$$J(x, y \mid u, v) = \frac{1}{J(u, v \mid x, y)}.$$

Extension to more variables is obvious.

For the case of planar polar coordinates, considered in Fig. 4–5, we have

$$x = u \cos\theta, \qquad y = u \sin\theta,$$

and

$$J(x, y \mid u, \theta) = \begin{vmatrix} \cos\theta & -u\sin\theta \\ \sin\theta & u\cos\theta \end{vmatrix} = u\cos^2\theta + u\sin^2\theta = u.$$

Thus

$$dx\, dy = u\, du\, d\theta.$$

Hence, the expression for the average relative speed becomes

$$\overline{v^{(\mathrm{rel})}} = \left(\frac{m}{2\pi kT}\right)^3 \int\!\cdots\!\int_{-\infty}^{+\infty} dv_x^{(12)}\, dv_y^{(12)}\, dv_z^{(12)} \exp\left(-\frac{m\{\mathbf{v}^{(12)}\}^2}{kT}\right)$$

$$\times \int\!\cdots\!\int_{-\infty}^{+\infty} dv_x^{(\mathrm{rel})}\, dv_y^{(\mathrm{rel})}\, dv_z^{(\mathrm{rel})} |\mathbf{v}^{\mathrm{rel}}| \exp\left(-\frac{m\{\mathbf{v}^{(\mathrm{rel})}\}^2}{4kT}\right),$$

$$= \frac{1}{8}\left(\frac{m}{\pi kT}\right)^{3/2} \int\!\cdots\!\int_{-\infty}^{+\infty} dv_x^{(\mathrm{rel})}\, dv_y^{(\mathrm{rel})}\, dv_z^{(\mathrm{rel})} |\mathbf{v}^{\mathrm{rel}}| \exp\left(-\frac{m\{\mathbf{v}^{(\mathrm{rel})}\}^2}{4kT}\right),$$

since the first integral is easily evaluated to be $(\pi kT/m)^{3/2}$.

The remaining integral is easily transformed to spherical polar coordinates, as in Eq. (4–36). Then if speeds are measured in units of $(kT/m)^{1/2}$ we obtain

$$\bar{s}_{\mathrm{rel}} = \frac{1}{2\sqrt{\pi}} \int_0^\infty ds_{\mathrm{rel}}\, s_{\mathrm{rel}}^3\, e^{-s_{\mathrm{rel}}^2/4} = \frac{4}{\sqrt{\pi}}, \qquad (4\text{–}51)$$

after carrying out the integration. Comparison with the average speed of a single molecule yields

$$\bar{s}_{rel} = \sqrt{2}\,\bar{s} = 2.259. \tag{4–52}$$

This relation between the average relative speed and the average speed looks *as if* the two molecules are each moving at the average speed in directions which are perpendicular to each other.

The extension to other multiple distributions in ideal gases follows along the lines indicated for pairs of molecules. We shall not consider them, however. The extension also to include effects of nonuniformity follows the arguments already exhibited in leading to the Maxwell-Boltzmann distribution. These considerations will be deferred for the present.

5. SUMMARY

In order to deal properly with molecular averages, we have examined some relations between probability and averaging. The use of a frequency distribution for this purpose has rendered the problem of molecular averaging into a general mathematical form useful for properties of variables that may have only distinct and separate values, or those having continuous ranges of values. In the latter case, distribution-density functions are used.

The hypotheses of the kinetic theory are translated into statistical terms. Specifically, the assumptions of isotropy and statistical independence of components of velocity of the molecules of an ideal gas lead to Maxwell's distribution of velocities. The distribution density is a product of three others, each of which is identical in form to the others but depends upon only one component of velocity. Various cases are discussed and averages are evaluated. Transformations to other coordinate systems are considered. A molecular-beam experiment is analyzed to provide experimental confirmation of the distribution law.

The Boltzmann distribution is considered as a consequence of the mechanical behavior of mass-points in equilibrium in an external potential field. This leads to the general Maxwell-Boltzmann distribution in velocity and position. The application to a calculation of barometric pressure at various altitudes provides a test of the relation.

The construction of multiple molecular distributions in ideal gases is examined as a simple extension of the idea of distributions in statistically independent variables. Here, the individual velocities of molecules are uncorrelated with one another, so that the multiple distribution is the product of individual Maxwell distributions.

EXERCISES

1. A distribution of pennies, nickles, dimes, and quarters is characterized by the following moments (in relevant units):

$$\bar{x} = 6.4, \qquad \overline{x^2} = 90.4, \qquad \overline{x^3} = 1800.4, \qquad \overline{x^4} = 41250.4,$$

where x is 1, 5, 10, or 25. Determine the distribution.
Answer: fr(1) = 0.40, fr(5) = 0.30, fr(10) = 0.20.

2. Compute the dispersion in coin values in the previous distribution.
Answer: $\overline{(x - \bar{x})^2} = 49.44$.

3. A frequently occurring distribution density (in y) is

$$f(y) = ce^{-cy},$$

which normalizes to unity in the interval $0 \leq y \leq +\infty$. Evaluate (a) the nth moment in y and (b) the dispersion in y.
Answers: (a) $\overline{y^n} = n!/c^n$; (b) $\overline{(y - \bar{y})^2} = 1/c^2$.

4. Renormalize the normal error curve to unity in the interval $0 \leq y \leq +\infty$ and pick a value of c in the previous distribution density so that both distributions yield the same mean value of the variable. Plot both curves and compare.
Answer: $c = \sqrt{\pi/2}$.

5. Determine the form of a statistically independent joint distribution whose density depends upon the product of the variables. That is,

$$\rho(xy) = \rho_1(x)\rho_1(y).$$

Answer: $\rho_1(u) \propto u^{\text{const}}$

6. Justify obtaining the normalized *effusive* distribution density:

$$\rho_{\text{eff}}\,(s, \theta, \phi) = \frac{1}{2\pi}\, s^3 \sin \theta \cos \theta e^{-s^2/2},$$

$$0 \leq \theta \leq \pi/2, \qquad 0 \leq \phi \leq 2\pi, \qquad 0 \leq s \leq +\infty.$$

(Consider that the Maxwell distribution is weighted according to the rates at which molecules of specified speeds and orientations effuse. See the argument involving Fig. 3–7.) This equation provides the basis for Eq. (4–39).

7. From the distribution of speeds in a collimated beam (i.e., the *effusive* distribution-in-speeds), determine the mean kinetic energy of an effusing molecule. Compare with the mean kinetic energy in the container.
Answer: $\bar{\epsilon}$ (effusing) = $2kT$.

8. Compute the mean rate of transport of momentum, per unit of area, in a gas effusing from a vessel at pressure P. (Note that the quantity of interest is $\bar{p}_{\text{eff}}\,\bar{v}$, where the former quantity is the mean value of the component of momentum normal to the hole in the effusing gas and the latter quantity is the mean effusing rate.) This result provides a means for measuring vapor pressures.
Answer: $\frac{1}{2}P$.

9. Construct a distribution-in-speeds from Eq. (4–37) by expressing the speeds in terms of the most probable speed, and plot in comparison with Fig. 4–10. *Answer:* $\rho(\sigma_0) \propto \sigma_0^2 e^{-\sigma_0^2}$.

10. The barometric formula may be used for ideal mixtures of ideal gases with the understanding that partial pressures are then implicit. Assume that at sea level, air consists of 70.00 mole percent nitrogen and 30.00 mole percent oxygen, and estimate the composition at an altitude of 20 km. (From Fig. 4–11, assume a mean temperature, regardless of altitude, of 220°K.) *Answer:* 70.09 mole percent nitrogen.

11. Consider the Maxwell-Boltzmann distribution for noninteracting particles constrained to move in a line in a uniform gravitational field. The energy of a particle is $(p^2/2m + mg\,z)$. Evaluate (a) the average kinetic energy of a particle, (b) the average potential energy of a particle, (c) the dispersion in position of a particle, and (d) the value of the latter at 300°K for H_2. *Answer:* (a) $\frac{1}{2}kT$; (b) kT; (c) $(kT/mg)^2$; (d) $1.6 \times 10^4\,\text{km}^2$.

12. (a) Demonstrate that the mean relative *velocity* of any pair of molecules in an ideal gas mixture is zero. (b) Show also that the mean value of the total momentum of any specified number of such molecules vanishes.

13. By successive integration by parts of Eq. (4–38), show that the fraction of molecules having kinetic energies in excess of some large value $E \gg kT$ is

$$\frac{2}{\sqrt{\pi}}\left(\frac{E}{kT}\right)^{1/2} e^{-E/kT}\left\{1 + \frac{1}{2}\left(\frac{kT}{E}\right) - \frac{1}{4}\left(\frac{kT}{E}\right)^2 + \cdots\right\}.$$

5 · NONIDEAL GASES

1. MODIFICATIONS OF IDEAL GAS THEORY

A drastic, but essential, simplification in the kinetic molecular theory of ideal gases is to be found in the assumption that molecules can be represented by structureless, noninteracting mass-points. The results obtained, however, justify such an *approximation* for real gases at low pressures. Nevertheless, as we shall see, not all properties of such gases can be deduced from the theory we have developed.

If we wish to extend the theory in a realistic manner, we must attribute to the molecules such structure and interactions as will be in accord with the observed behavior of real gases. Conversely, certain aspects of real gas behavior suggest what is to be done. In particular, the existence of both positive and negative deviations from ideality point to the basic assumption to be made for real molecules. It seems reasonable, as suggested by the partial success of a covolume equation of state, discussed in Chapter 1, to suppose that the *size* of the molecules must be incorporated into the theory. But how is this to be done?

The size of an object implicitly relates to the means of its measurement. For molecules, a direct measurement of their sizes seems unlikely. However, a *conceptual* means of measurement obviates the practical difficulty. If we take a spherical ball made of sponge rubber, we can *see* how large it is. If we attempt to measure its size with the aid of a micrometer, the reading will depend upon how much deformation of the ball is involved. However, both the visual and mechanical sizes can be made to coincide (within experimental error) if the latter corresponds to no deformation. Since deformation will generally result from the application of a force, and increases with increasing force, we may take the size of the ball to correspond to that measured under conditions of essentially no applied force. However, in more general terms, we can avoid the explicit statement of size, while retaining the idea, by giving the *potential energy* function of the interaction between the ball and the jaws of the micrometer. From Eq. (3–9), the force can be computed. Clearly, to be able to resist the deformation the computed force must be positive, or repulsive.

The negative deviations from ideality point to an inherent attraction between molecules. Otherwise, how can one account for condensation of a vapor to form a macroscopically stable liquid? Since the compressibility of liquids is usually small, the attractive nature of molecules is rather

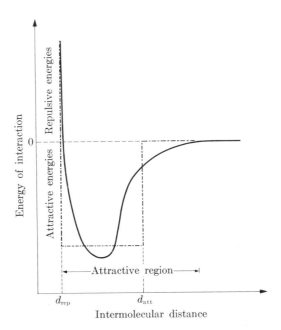

Fig. 5–1. Intermolecular potential shape.

limited. As molecules of a liquid are forced closer together, the size effect begins to assert its influence.

These qualitative notions can be summarized in the form of an *inter-molecular potential* between molecules. Such a potential is indicated qualitatively in Fig. 5–1. It can be correct only for molecules whose interactions *are independent of their shapes*. It pertains to atoms and, with good approximation, to essentially spherical molecules. The value of zero has been identified with the interaction at indefinitely large distances. The "size" of the molecules appears only implicitly, by the presence of repulsion. Although the actual shape of the intermolecular potential may vary from one pair of molecules to another, the features of importance remaining are:

1. The interaction potential vanishes for sufficiently large intermolecular distances.

2. In a certain range of intermolecular distances, the potential is attractive.

3. For distances smaller than some value, the potential is repulsive.

These properties are likewise manifested by the potential represented by the dashed curve in Fig. 5–1.

Modifications of the potential energy function by the shape of the molecules are to be expected. We shall not deal with them, however, except to stress the fact that molecules can be *bound* to each other (pair-wise) only if the value of their total energy of relative motion is nonpositive. Otherwise, there is always the possibility that a given value of the total energy will correspond to a zero value of the potential energy and positive kinetic energy. Hence, unbound molecules will result.

2. APPLICATION TO INTRAMOLECULAR MOTION

The simplest situation that permits a test of the above ideas occurs at low pressures in gases which consist of *diatomic molecules*. With respect to their atomic constituents, bound as they are to each other in pairs, the gas behavior is nonideal. Yet, with respect to the molecules, the gaseous behavior may be regarded as ideal. In other words, we may imagine a strong interaction between a pair of atoms, as represented by Fig. 5–1, while the interaction between any two diatomic molecules is practically negligible.

If there were no interaction between the atoms, we should be able to discuss the behavior of the pair in terms of the pair distribution density expressed in Eq. (4–48). In fact, we already have done this. When the two atoms do interact, the pair distribution density must be modified along the lines leading to the Maxwell-Boltzmann formula, Eq. (4–44). To make this modification, we recognize that the total energy of the molecule must replace the total kinetic energy in Eq. (4–48). Moreover, since we are restricting our attention to a *single molecule*, it will be convenient to deal with a *probability* distribution density. Hence, the probability density of finding a pair of atoms of masses m_1 and m_2 with velocities in the range of $\mathbf{v}^{(1)}$ and $\mathbf{v}^{(2)}$ and positions in the range of $\mathbf{r}^{(1)}$ and $\mathbf{r}^{(2)}$ is

$$\rho_2(\mathbf{v}^{(1)}, \mathbf{v}^{(2)}, \mathbf{r}^{(1)}, \mathbf{r}^{(2)}) = C \left(\frac{m_1}{2\pi kT}\right)^{3/2} \left(\frac{m_2}{2\pi kT}\right)^{3/2}$$

$$\times \exp\left(-\frac{[(m_1/2)\{\mathbf{v}^{(1)}\}^2 + (m_2/2)\{\mathbf{v}^{(2)}\}^2 + \phi]}{kT}\right), \quad (5\text{–}1)$$

where

$$\phi \equiv \phi(|\mathbf{r}^{(1)} - \mathbf{r}^{(2)}|) \qquad (5\text{–}2)$$

is the interatomic potential energy and is regarded as a function of the interatomic distance, as in Fig. 5–1, while C is a constant chosen so that

$$\int \cdots \int dv_x^{(1)} \, dv_y^{(1)} \, dv_z^{(1)} \, dv_x^{(2)} \, dv_y^{(2)} \, dv_z^{(2)} \, dx^{(1)} \, dy^{(1)} \, dz^{(1)} \, dx^{(2)} \, dy^{(2)} \, dz^{(2)} \rho_2 = 1.$$

(all possible
values)
$$(5\text{–}3)$$

It is easy to see that when ϕ vanishes, as for noninteracting atoms, $1/C$

must be equal to V^2, the square of the volume of the container, which yields Eq. (4–48).

We can transform to the coordinates of the center of mass and relative distance:

$$\mathbf{r}^{(12)} = \frac{m_1 \mathbf{r}^{(1)} + m_2 \mathbf{r}^{(2)}}{m_1 + m_2}$$

and

$$\mathbf{r}^{(\text{rel})} = \mathbf{r}^{(1)} - \mathbf{r}^{(2)},$$

noting that

$$\mathbf{v}^{(12)} = \dot{\mathbf{r}}^{(12)}, \quad \text{and} \quad \mathbf{v}^{(\text{rel})} = \dot{\mathbf{r}}^{(\text{rel})}.$$

If we write

$$M = m_1 + m_2 \quad \text{and} \quad \mu = \frac{m_1 m_2}{M},$$

we obtain

$$\rho_2 = C\left[\left(\frac{M}{2\pi kT}\right)^{3/2} \exp\left(-\frac{M}{2kT}\{\mathbf{v}^{(12)}\}^2\right)\right]$$

$$\times \left[\left(\frac{\mu}{2\pi kT}\right)^{3/2} \exp\left(-\frac{\mu}{2kT}\{\mathbf{v}^{(\text{rel})}\}^2 - \frac{\phi(|\mathbf{r}^{(\text{rel})}|)}{kT}\right)\right]. \tag{5–4}$$

The differential volume element is

$$d\mathbf{v}^{(12)}\, d\mathbf{v}^{(\text{rel})}\, d\mathbf{r}^{(12)}\, d\mathbf{r}^{(\text{rel})} = dv_x^{(12)}\, dv_y^{(12)}\, dv_z^{(12)}\, dv_x^{(\text{rel})}\, dv_y^{(\text{rel})}\, dv_z^{(\text{rel})}$$

$$\times\, dx^{(12)}\, dy^{(12)}\, dz^{(12)}\, dx^{(\text{rel})}\, dy^{(\text{rel})}\, dz^{(\text{rel})}.$$

In the absence of an external potential, the distribution density is independent of the location of the center of mass. The first bracketed factor in Eq. (5–4) can be recognized as the Maxwell distribution density, Eq. (4–31a), of velocity of the center of mass of the molecule, while the second bracketed factor relates to the internal motion of the molecule. The ideal gas properties of the molecules are contained, so to say, in the first factor and we have already examined these in the previous chapter. We shall therefore restrict our attention to the last factor.

We define the *internal distribution density* as

$$\rho_{\text{int}}(\mathbf{v}^{(\text{rel})}, \mathbf{r}^{(\text{rel})}) = C\left(\frac{\mu}{2\pi kT}\right)^{3/2} \exp\left[-\frac{\mu}{2kT}\{\mathbf{v}^{(\text{rel})}\}^2 - \frac{\phi(|\mathbf{r}^{(\text{rel})}|)}{kT}\right]. \tag{5–5}$$

In order to exhibit the feature that Eq. (5–6) is related to a *molecule*, rather than to two atoms, it will be useful to work in spherical polar coordinates. Since the motion of the center of mass has been abstracted in Eq. (5–5), it also is convenient to work in a center-of-mass representation, as discussed in Chapter 3. A schematic diagram of the motion of a

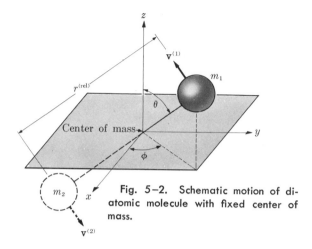

Fig. 5–2. Schematic motion of diatomic molecule with fixed center of mass.

diatomic molecule is shown in Fig. 5–2. (The diagram is correct for determining *relative velocities* and *distances* even if the center of mass is moving. However, the individual velocities and positions of each atom require a knowledge of the corresponding values for the center of mass.) The motion of a diatomic molecule is a composite of rotation about the origin and that due to changes in its interatomic distance. In this coordinate system, the center of mass is regarded as stationary. Hence,

$$m_1 \mathbf{r}^{(1)} + m_2 \mathbf{r}^{(2)} = 0. \tag{5–6}$$

Therefore,

$$\mathbf{r}^{(\text{rel})} = \mathbf{r}^{(1)} - \mathbf{r}^{(2)} = \left(1 + \frac{m_1}{m_2}\right)\mathbf{r}^{(1)} = \left(\frac{M}{m_2}\right)\mathbf{r}^{(1)}. \tag{5–7}$$

Because the time derivative of position is the velocity of motion, we have

$$\mathbf{v}^{(\text{rel})} = \left(\frac{M}{m_2}\right)\dot{\mathbf{r}}^{(1)}. \tag{5–8}$$

Now, in the present coordinate system

$$x^{(1)} = r^{(1)} \sin \theta \cos \phi,$$
$$y^{(1)} = r^{(1)} \sin \theta \sin \phi,$$
$$z^{(1)} = r^{(1)} \cos \theta.$$

Therefore,

$$\dot{x}^{(1)} = \sin \theta \cos \phi \, \dot{r}^{(1)} + r^{(1)} \cos \theta \cos \phi \, \dot{\theta} - r^{(1)} \sin \theta \sin \phi \, \dot{\phi},$$
$$\dot{y}^{(1)} = \sin \theta \sin \phi \, \dot{r}^{(1)} + r^{(1)} \cos \theta \sin \phi \, \dot{\theta} + r^{(1)} \sin \theta \cos \phi \, \dot{\phi},$$
$$\dot{z}^{(1)} = \qquad \cos \theta \, \dot{r}^{(1)} - r^{(1)} \sin \theta \, \dot{\theta}.$$

When the necessary multiplications and additions are carried out, we can obtain

$$\{\dot{\mathbf{r}}^{(1)}\}^2 = \{\dot{x}^{(1)}\}^2 + \{\dot{y}^{(1)}\}^2 + \{\dot{z}^{(1)}\}^2$$
$$= \{\dot{r}^{(1)}\}^2 + \{r^{(1)}\}^2\{\dot{\theta}\}^2 + \{r^{(1)}\sin\theta\}^2\{\dot{\phi}\}^2.$$

The last two terms relate to the rotational motion of the molecule. From Eqs. (5–6) through (5–8) and the definition of the reduced mass, we obtain

$$\frac{\mu}{2}\{\mathbf{v}^{(\text{rel})}\}^2 = \frac{\mu}{2}(\dot{r}^{(\text{rel})})^2 + \frac{\mu\{r^{(\text{rel})}\}^2}{2}[\{\dot{\theta}\}^2 + \sin^2\theta\{\dot{\phi}\}^2]. \quad (5\text{–}9)$$

In order to utilize the internal distribution density, Eq. (5–5), we need the volume element in the above coordinates:

$$d\mathbf{v}^{(\text{rel})}\,d\mathbf{r}^{(\text{rel})} = J\,dr^{(\text{rel})}\,d\theta\,d\phi\,d\dot{r}^{(\text{rel})}\,d\dot{\theta}\,d\dot{\phi}.$$

An evaluation of the Jacobian ultimately gives

$$d\mathbf{v}^{(\text{rel})}\,d\mathbf{r}^{(\text{rel})} = \{r^{(\text{rel})}\}^4\sin^2\theta\,dr^{(\text{rel})}\,d\theta\,d\phi\,d\dot{r}^{(\text{rel})}\,d\dot{\theta}\,d\dot{\phi}.$$

With this volume element and Eq. (5–6), the *mean energy* of *intramolecular motion* can be evaluated.

Before we carry out this program, however, we must pay attention to the restrictions which are imposed by the fact that we are dealing with a molecule. It is especially obvious that $r^{(\text{rel})}$ is restricted to a finite range of values if the atoms are to be regarded as bound to one another. Furthermore, the speed of relative motion, $v^{(\text{rel})}$, also must be restricted to a finite range of values, if the interatomic potential of Fig. 5–2 is considered. Otherwise the kinetic energy of relative motion would ultimately acquire such large values that the total energy of relative motion would be positive, corresponding to unbound atoms. For these reasons, it is advisable to deal separately with the rotational motion and the interatomic motion (we shall refer to the latter as *vibrational* motion).

If the potential energy function $\phi(r^{(\text{rel})})$ is restricted to negative values in an extremely small range of interatomic distances, and it has very large negative values there, the variation of interatomic distance will be extremely small. This behavior means that the distribution density, Eq. (5–5), will have extremely small values except in the permitted range of interatomic distances. In the limit that no variation of interatomic distance is possible, no relative speed is possible, and we have the case of a *rigid rotor*. For such a molecule, the *rotational distribution density* can be written as

$$\rho_{\text{rot}}(\theta, \phi, \dot{\theta}, \dot{\phi}) = C\exp\left(-\frac{\mu r_0^2}{2kT}[\{\dot{\theta}\}^2 + \sin^2\theta\{\dot{\phi}\}^2]\right), \quad (5\text{–}10)$$

where r_0 is the *equilibrium interatomic* distance. To satisfy Eq. (5–3), we require that

$$\int_{-\infty}^{+\infty} d\dot{\theta} \int_{-\infty}^{+\infty} d\dot{\phi} \int_0^{\pi} d\theta \sin^2 \theta \int_0^{2\pi} d\phi \, \rho_{\rm rot}(\theta, \phi, \dot{\theta}, \dot{\phi}) = 1,$$

which gives

$$C = \frac{\mu r_0^2}{8\pi^2 kT}.$$

The quantity

$$\mu r_0^2 = m_1 \{r_0^{(1)}\}^2 + m_2 \{r_0^{(2)}\}^2, \qquad (5\text{–}11)$$

by Eq. (5–6) and Fig. 5–2, is the *moment of inertia* of the molecule. The average rotational energy is

$$\bar{\epsilon}_{\rm rot} = \frac{\mu r_0^2}{8\pi^2 kT} \int_{-\infty}^{+\infty} d\dot{\theta} \int_{-\infty}^{+\infty} d\dot{\phi} \int_0^{\pi} d\theta \sin^2 \theta \int_0^{2\pi} d\phi$$

$$\times \frac{\mu r_0^2}{2} [\{\dot{\theta}\}^2 + \sin^2 \theta \{\dot{\phi}\}^2] \exp\left(-\frac{\mu r_0^2}{2kT}[\{\dot{\theta}\}^2 + \sin^2 \theta \{\dot{\phi}\}^2]\right)$$

$$= \frac{kT}{2\pi} \int_{-\infty}^{+\infty} ds \int_{-\infty}^{+\infty} dt \, \frac{(s^2 + t^2)}{2} e^{-(s^2+t^2)/2},$$

where the integral has been transformed by setting

$$s = \left(\frac{\mu r_0^2}{kT}\right)^{1/2} \dot{\theta} \qquad \text{and} \qquad t = \left(\frac{\mu r_0^2}{kT}\right)^{1/2} \sin \theta \dot{\phi}.$$

The integral is one we already have encountered for a two-dimensional Maxwell distribution, Fig. 4–4. Hence,

$$\bar{\epsilon}_{\rm rot} = kT. \qquad (5\text{–}12)$$

From Eq. (3–53), we have for the total energy of a rigid diatomic molecule,

$$\bar{\epsilon}_{\rm trans} + \bar{\epsilon}_{\rm rot} = \tfrac{5}{2}kT. \qquad (5\text{–}13)$$

For such molecules, we should expect that their heat capacities at constant volume are

$$(C_v)_{\rm trans+rot} = \tfrac{5}{2}R = 4.97 \text{ cal/gm-mole·°K}. \qquad (5\text{–}14)$$

From Table 5–1, surprisingly good agreement is observed for a variety of diatomic molecules at room temperature. Nevertheless, certain discrepancies are evident.

TABLE 5–1

HEAT CAPACITIES AT CONSTANT VOLUME FOR SOME
POLYATOMIC MOLECULES AT 15°C*

Gas	C_V, cal/gm-mole·°K
H_2	4.87
N_2	4.93
O_2	5.04
NO	5.00
CO	4.94
NH_3	6.67
CH_4	6.48
H_2S	6.08
CO_2	6.75

* Data from *Handbook of Chemistry and Physics*. Cleveland: Chemical Rubber Publishing Co.

The most astonishing consequence of Table 5–1 is the *absence of significant contributions due to vibrational motion of the atoms*. Although our formulas have been derived for rigid diatomic molecules, it is quite unlikely that there are any! Any general results must invoke the exact form of the interatomic potential. Nevertheless, if an analysis is carried through, it will be found that whatever contribution is made by vibratory motion to the heat capacity, it exceeds the observed contribution enormously. The rigid model we have adopted is seemingly adequate to account for the properties of diatomic molecules. It appears as though the vibratory motion is *quenched*. This apparent inadequacy of the theory is now understood in terms of the *quantum mechanics* of molecular motion. In terms of this mechanics, not all energies of molecular motion are possible. Separation into independently variable kinetic and potential energy contributions is not possible. Consequently, the analysis we have given is approximate, in an ultimate sense. This is evident from the behavior observed in the heat capacity at constant volume for hydrogen. At very small temperatures, the heat capacity approaches that of a monatomic gas, indicating that the "quenching" noted for vibratory motion also occurs with rotational motion. Indeed, this behavior is now regarded as universal for all sorts of motion: At sufficiently small temperatures, depending upon the kind of motion, the contribution made to the molecular heat capacity by various kinds of motion will be negligible. At sufficiently large temperatures, the behavior of *quantum systems* conforms to the statistical behavior we have described.

For our purposes, we shall omit a discussion of quantum effects. Instead, we shall remark briefly upon the behavior to be anticipated for *polyatomic molecules* at temperatures which are large enough for the validity of our analysis of translational and rotational motion, but small enough so that vibratory motion is effectively quenched. In such cases, the contribution to the energy of a molecule is related to the number of *kinetic energy* terms appearing. From the case considered, there will be three such terms for the center of mass and two for the rotational motion. Indeed, such will be the case for any *linear* molecule. For nonlinear molecules, it can be shown (although we shall not do so) that rotational energies involve one more term than in the linear case. In fact, the motion of spinning a linear molecule on its interatomic axis has been tacitly suppressed, and it is this motion which becomes manifest in nonlinear molecules. For each of these kinetic energy terms, there appears a square of a velocity. Each such term, as we have seen, contributes a value of $kT/2$ to the mean molecular energy, *regardless of its actual nature*.

This result is applicable to terms of the potential energy which are also quadratic in the displacement. The general statement is embodied in an *equipartition theorem:* for each energy term which is quadratic in a velocity component or position component there is a contribution of $kT/2$ to the mean energy. Each such contribution refers to a *single degree of freedom* of the system.

Hence we have for nonlinear molecules that

$$(C_v)_{\text{trans+rot}} = 3R = 5.96 \text{ cal/gm-mole·°K.} \qquad (5\text{-}15)$$

Values in Table 5-1 are reasonably in accord with this result. However, the agreement leaves something to be desired. From our previous remarks, it should be evident that the over-all heat capacity is a complicated admixture of various contributions. Some are quenched only incompletely at ordinary temperatures and give rise to values slightly in excess of the value of Eq. (5-15). When a proper quantum analysis is made, good agreement between theory and experiment is obtained.

Historically, the anomalous behavior in the heat capacities of diatomic gases was first pointed out by Boltzmann in 1876. His ideas were rejected strenuously by reputable scientists of the time in spite of their essential correctness, as now understood.

3. MOLECULAR COLLISIONS

One of the most important effects of molecular interactions lies in the resulting collisions that molecules experience with each other as they move through a gas. As we have seen in Chapter 3, the effect of collisions is to change the direction and speeds of the colliding molecules. However, the changes occurring are presumed to maintain equality of the initial and final values of the kinetic energy of the pair. Such collisions are referred to as *elastic* collisions. Because the molecules of a gas may be polyatomic, it is possible that the internal motions of the colliding molecules may be altered, with a corresponding change in their energies of internal motion. In such cases, the collisions are termed *inelastic*. We shall confine our attention to elastic collisions.

From the analysis given in Chapter 3, we know that a pairwise collision can be represented as occurring in a plane if the intermolecular potential depends only upon the distance between the particles. Moreover, we can work in a center-of-mass representation to simplify the visualization of the motion exhibited by the particles. Because of Eq. (5–7), the motion can be regarded as that of a *single particle* colliding with a *fixed central force field*. This is indicated in Fig. 5–3, for the potential of Fig. 5–1.

For a finite range of force, there is a maximum distance of closest approach of the colliding molecules; for greater distances there is no deflection of their paths and, hence, no collision. Clearly, however, it is possible to imagine for certain distances of closest approach undeflected trajectories that depend upon the relative kinetic energy of the pair. As a consequence, each of a pair of molecules presents to the other a target area for deflecting collisions which may depend upon their relative kinetic energy, in general. We shall disregard this feature, for reasons of simplicity, and associate with each pair of colliding molecules an

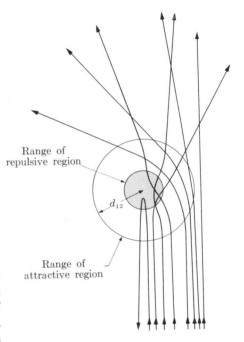

Fig. 5–3. Schematic trajectories of a scattered particle.

impenetrable sphere of diameter d_{12}. In an approximate way, the diameter of this sphere is equal to the sum of the *radii* of the individual molecules engaging in the collision.

The frequency with which a specified molecule will collide with other molecules of the gas may now be calculated. For each value of relative speed, $|\mathbf{v}^{(rel)}|$, the molecules in a volume $\pi\, d_{12}^2 |\mathbf{v}^{(rel)}|$ will collide with the specified molecule. This arises from the fact that a given molecule moving through the gas may be struck from any direction by molecules moving toward it. Therefore, only the relative speed matters and the averaging must include all such values and directions. [For this reason, the similar argument in Chapter 3, for the effusion rate, has a factor of $\frac{1}{2}$ in Eq. (3–61) and a factor of $\frac{1}{4}$ in Eq. (3–62).] Hence, the average *frequency of collisions with a specified molecule* is

$$\bar{\nu}_1 = \left(\frac{n}{V}\right) \pi d_{12}^2 \overline{|\mathbf{v}^{(\mathrm{rel})}|} = \sqrt{2} \left(\frac{n}{V}\right) \pi d_{12}^2 \overline{|\mathbf{v}|}$$

$$= \left(\frac{n}{V}\right) 4\pi d_{12}^2 \left(\frac{kT}{\pi m}\right)^{1/2} = \frac{4\pi d_{12}^2 P}{(\pi m kT)^{1/2}}, \qquad (5\text{–}16)$$

on the assumption that all the masses are equal, as in Eq. (4–52). Because energy is conserved in a collision and the range of forces is finite, Maxwell's distribution can be used for the averaging. (When molecules of different masses are involved, m is replaced by twice the reduced mass of the colliding pair.)

The total number of binary collisions in the gas is found by summing Eq. (5–16) over all molecules and halving the result to eliminate a double count. For identical molecules we have for the mean *binary collision frequency per unit volume*

$$\bar{\nu}_{11} = \left(\frac{n}{V}\right)^2 2\pi d_{12}^2 \left(\frac{kT}{\pi m}\right)^{1/2} = \frac{2\pi d_{12}^2 P^2}{kT(\pi m kT)^{1/2}}. \qquad (5\text{–}17a)$$

When the mean binary collision frequency for *different* molecules is desired, the previous formula becomes

$$\bar{\nu}_{12} = \left(\frac{n_1}{V}\right)\left(\frac{n_2}{V}\right) 4\pi d_{12}^2 \left(\frac{kT}{2\pi \mu}\right)^{1/2} = \frac{4\pi d_{12}^2 P_1 P_2}{kT(2\pi \mu kT)^{1/2}}, \qquad (5\text{–}17b)$$

where the subscripts refer to the two gases, with μ the reduced mass of the pair of molecules.

From the mean frequency of collisions of a single molecule, $\bar{\nu}_1$, we see that the mean time interval between collisions is

$$\tau = \frac{1}{\bar{\nu}_1}.$$

During this interval, the molecules move through a distance which is called the *mean free path*, λ. We have, therefore, that

$$\lambda = \frac{\overline{|\mathbf{v}|}}{\bar{\nu}_1} = \frac{\sqrt{2}}{2\pi d_{12}^2 (n/V)} = \frac{\sqrt{2}\, kT}{2\pi d_{12}^2 P}. \qquad (5\text{–}18)$$

It is noteworthy that the mean free path depends only upon the number density of the gas and the size of the molecules.

From the molal volume of a liquid, we are able to get some estimate of the size of its molecules. If we take for the molal volume a value of about 50 ml/gm-mole, the diameter of a spherical molecule will be approximately 5×10^{-8} cm. At standard conditions of temperature and pressure, (n/V) is approximately 2.7×10^{19} molecules/cm^3. As a result, we see from Eq. (5–18) that λ is of the order of 3×10^{-6} cm, an extremely small distance under standard conditions of temperature and pressure. With such a value of the mean free path, a molecule of hydrogen gas will experience approximately 10^{11} collisions/second. Under the same conditions, the binary collision frequency for hydrogen molecules is approximately 10^{30} collisions/sec·cm^3.

The quantity

$$\sigma_{12} = \pi d_{12}^2$$

is sometimes referred to as the *scattering cross section* of the molecules. It is a quantity which can be measured directly, in principle. To see how this may be done, we shall simplify matters somewhat. We imagine a beam of molecules, as in Fig. 4–8, entering a container of gas. The beam detector has an extremely small aperture, and so will admit only those molecules which have not been scattered in their passage through the gas. The measurements which are made yield the intensity of the beam (proportional to the number of undeflected molecules reaching the detector in a unit of time) as a function of the distance traversed by the beam. The apparatus is sketched in Fig. 5–4.

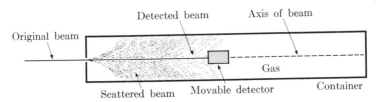

Fig. 5–4. Scattering of molecular beam by gas.

We can guess how the measured intensity, $I(x)$, must vary with the distance x, as follows. Clearly, the effect of doubling the initial intensity will be to double the intensity at every point on the axis. This situation is identical with the effect to be expected if the beam molecules do not interact with one another, which is the case in practice, and two identical beams replace the original one. In mathematical terms, we have

$$\frac{I(x)}{I(0)} = f(x) \text{ alone},$$

where $I(0)$ refers to the initial beam intensity. However, we may always regard any point on the axis between the source and the detector as the origin, so that

$$\frac{I(x)}{I(x_0)} = f(x - x_0), \tag{5–19}$$

where $0 \le x_0 \le x$. For Eq. (5–19) to be valid for all (x_0, x) we must require that

$$\frac{I'(x)}{I(x_0)} = f'(x - x_0),$$

and

$$-\frac{I(x)}{I^2(x_0)} I'(x_0) = -f'(x - x_0),$$

which equations result from differentiation of Eq. (5–19) with respect to x and x_0, respectively. These equations yield

$$\frac{I'(x)}{I(x)} = \frac{I'(x_0)}{I(x_0)} = -K, \quad \text{indep. of } (x_0, x).$$

Integration of this equation is easily carried out and ultimately yields

$$I(x) = I(x_0)e^{-K(x-x_0)}. \tag{5–20}$$

The constant K must be *positive* in order to have a beam of decreasing intensity.

Now $\{I(x)/I(x_0)\}$ is simply the *survival fraction* of beam molecules at x_0 which reach x without collision or scattering. The fraction of original molecules which are scattered by the time the unscattered molecules reach x is $\{1 - [I(x)/I(x_0)]\}$. Clearly, the *mortality fraction* is given by

$$M = \left\{1 - \frac{I(x)}{I(x_0)}\right\} = \int_0^{x-x_0} dy\, K e^{-Ky},$$

and $Ke^{-K(x-x_0)}$ is the probability density of a molecule being scattered in the beam length x to $x + dx$. This is evident from the expression

$$dM = Ke^{-K(x-x_0)}\, dx. \tag{5–21}$$

This expression may also be understood as the probability density that a beam molecule will have a free path length in the range of $(x - x_0)$. The mean free path can be identified as the average distance a beam molecule will travel before it is scattered. Hence,

$$\lambda = \int_{M=0}^{M=1} (x - x_0)\, dM = \int_{x_0}^{\infty} dx\, (x - x_0)e^{-K(x-x_0)} = \frac{1}{K}. \tag{5–22}$$

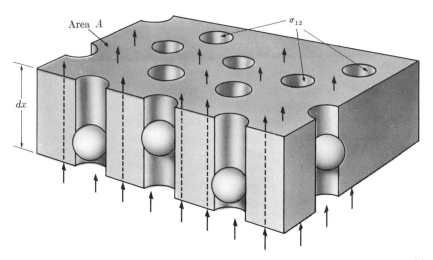

Fig. 5–5. View of beam passing gas molecules. Shaded regions are impenetrable.

We may now employ Eq. (5–21) to evaluate λ in terms of molecular properties. To do this, we observe that the quantity $dM/e^{-(x-x_0)/\lambda}$ is the relative loss of beam molecules in going from x to $x + dx$. In terms of Fig. 5–5, this loss is to be equated to the relative cross-sectional area which impedes passage of the beam. This, in turn, is related to the total number of molecules which can be overtaken by the beam in traversing the distance dx. (Otherwise, there can be no collision and no scattering.) If the molecules of the gas were stationary, it is evident that the number overtaken by the beam would be simply $(n/V)A\,dx$, where (n/V) is the molecular density. However, if the molecules are moving relative to the beam, as they are, the actual number overtaken by the beam in a unit of time varies with their velocity. Let $\mathbf{v}$ be their velocity and let $\mathbf{v}_0$ be the velocity of the beam molecules. Then, the number of molecules overtaken when the beam sweeps out a volume $A\,dx$ is $(n/V)(|\mathbf{v}_0 - \mathbf{v}|/v_0)A\,dx$. This corresponds to a relative projected area of $(n/V)(|\mathbf{v}_0 - \mathbf{v}|/v_0)\sigma_{12}\,dx$. This quantity must be averaged over the distribution in velocity for the gas molecules to be overtaken (or vice versa) and equated to $K\,dx$.

For a Maxwellian distribution we need, for fixed v_0,

$$\overline{\frac{|\mathbf{v}_0 - \mathbf{v}|}{v_0}} = \left(\frac{m}{2\pi kT}\right)^{3/2} \int\!\!\!\int\!\!\!\int_{-\infty}^{+\infty} dv_x\,dv_y\,dv_z\,\frac{|\mathbf{v}_0 - \mathbf{v}|}{v_0}\,e^{-mv^2/2kT}, \quad (5\text{–}23)$$

making use of Eq. (4–31a). Representing the left side of Eq. (5–23) by the quantity β, we can establish that β, which depends upon v_0 and (kT/m), is not less than unity. In any case, the mean relative area projected is

$(n/V)\beta\sigma_{12} \, dx$. Upon identifying this with Eqs. (5–21) and (5–22), we obtain

$$\lambda = \frac{1}{\beta\sigma_{12}(n/V)} = \frac{1}{\beta\pi \, d_{12}^2(n/V)} \, . \qquad (5\text{–}24)$$

This expression depends *implicitly upon the beam velocity*. It may be seen to be identical *in form* with Eq. (5–18). When β is averaged over all beam velocities, we may anticipate the value given in that equation, although we shall not derive it.

While the discussion has centered around scattering as measured by a deflection of beam particles from their original direction, it may be generalized to other kinds. Thus, one may be interested in how far a beam molecule of a certain internal energy will travel before it exchanges this energy by collisions with other molecules. When it is experimentally possible to measure the beam intensity according to the internal energy of the molecules, precisely the above analysis pertains. The mean free paths of the beam molecules may, however, vary according to the process of interest. In the present illustration, this simply signifies that the likelihood of deflection by collision may differ from the likelihood of internal energy exchange upon collision. Alternatively, the cross sections for the two processes may differ, and usually do.

4. SIMPLE THEORY OF TRANSPORT PROPERTIES

We now are in a position to examine the kinetic behavior of a gas as related to the properties of thermal conductivity, diffusion, and viscosity. As discussed in Chapter 2, and emphasized by the correlations in Figs. 2–9 and 2–10, we can anticipate that these transport properties have a common feature: the passage of molecules through the gas.

As the molecules of a gas move about, they collide with one another and so interchange energy and momentum. The total values of these quantities are unaltered by the collisions, but the collisions serve as an *equilibrating mechanism* in the sense that less energetic partners tend to gain energy at the expense of loss by their more energetic partners. We have seen how this occurs for particles in head-on collisions, in Chapter 4. When the *average* properties of each of the colliding members are all the same, no changes of an *average* sort are expected and a uniform steady state of the gas is achieved. When, however, the colliding members originate from regions with different average properties of energy and momentum, the net effect of collisions is to promote a transfer of these quantities from one region to another. Ultimately, the transfer must be maintained by external means.

A proper analysis of transport phenomena in gases must involve the knowledge of three things:

1. The relation between averages of mechanical properties of the molecules *in each region*, and the macroscopic properties of temperature, pressure, and composition there.

2. The mean rates at which molecules move from one region of a gas to another.

3. The mean effectiveness of transfer of energy, momentum, and composition upon collision in various regions.

When the gas is in a uniform steady state, estimates of each of these quantities can be made. Our previous analysis has provided some of the answers. However, because of the very existence of transport, we are certain that these answers cannot be entirely correct. Our previous results have employed the Maxwell-Boltzmann distribution and the latter has relied heavily upon considerations of motional isotropy of a gas as determining the distribution in velocity. The *anisotropy in velocities* accompanying the transport of molecules emphasizes the inadequacy of the Maxwell distribution. Both (1) and (2), above, are affected by the velocity distribution. Moreover, it is evident that (3) relates to the *determination* of the velocity distribution, so the precise analysis of transport can be identified with the determination of the velocity distribution in nonuniform gases.

The changes which must be made in the velocity distribution can, in principle, be determined by a method introduced by Boltzmann. As a consequence of his investigations into the dynamics of molecular collisions, he was able to deduce what is now known as the *Boltzmann equation* for the time rate of change of the distribution density. The general integration of this equation has not yet been effected, although good approximations in many important cases are available. For uniform gases, the Maxwell velocity distribution is obtained, providing additional theoretical support of its validity.

In more general terms, however, the physical feature that proves important in altering the velocity distribution relates to the *persistence of velocities* during collisions. As we have seen in Chapter 4, the transfer of energy in a collision of mass-points depends upon the relative masses and velocities of the colliding particles. This is also true for particles of nonzero size. When the kinetic energy of one of the colliding molecules is large, the transfer is relatively small. Hence the effectiveness of a collision as an equilibrating mechanism varies with the kinetic energy of the molecules, being less effective for those with larger kinetic energies. From this point of view, molecules with large velocities will have *effectively* longer free paths for *the equilibration process* than we have considered. In turn, this means also that the effective cross section which must be used depends upon the kind of process under investigation, e.g., whether it is equilibration with respect to energy, or with respect to momentum.

Although it is not exact in the present situation, the Maxwell distribution in velocities should be a reasonable approximation to the one obtaining in a nonuniform gas. As long as the particle density of the gas is large enough, one can be assured of meaningful values of temperature, pressure, and composition in each region of the gas. When gradients of these quantities are small, only slight deviations from the Maxwell velocity distribution can be anticipated. Its use, however, in the problems at hand involves an approximation that can involve only a lack of quantitative agreement between theory and experiment: the physical ideas involved are correct. Consequently, the simple theory we propose to construct will be useful, in spite of its quantitative limitations, for understanding the transport properties of gases in terms of the behavior of their constituent molecules.

We wish, first of all, to examine the net rate at which molecules flow past a plane of unit area in the gas. Since we already know the result for a uniform gas, as in Eq. (3–63), we will have a first check on the ideas involved. However, we wish to incorporate the facts of collision in this analysis. In any small volume element we may suppose that there are an enormous number of collisions which are effective in promoting equilibration of energy, momentum, or composition, as the case may be. [See the estimates following Eq. (5–18).] The appropriate mean collision frequency is given by $\bar{\nu}_{11}$ or $\bar{\nu}_{12}$, Eqs. (5–17a) and (5–17b). In Fig. 5–6, these collisions are assumed to occur in the indicated volume element. The mean number of colliding molecules leaving the volume element, in unit time, is assumed to be $2\bar{\nu}_{11}\,dV$ or $2\bar{\nu}_{12}\,dV$. Of these, only those moving in the direction of the plane of area A are capable of passing through it. Assuming that the colliding molecules leave isotropically, the capable fraction is simply the ratio of the area normal to r, the distance of the source to the plane, to the area of a sphere of the same radius. For small A, this is $A\cos\theta/4\pi r^2$. Of these molecules, only the fraction $e^{-r/\lambda}$ will survive the passage without collision. Hence the small mean rate of passage of molecules through A, per unit area, is

$$d\bar{\nu} = \frac{\bar{\nu}_{11}\cos\theta}{2\pi r^2}\,e^{-r/\lambda}\,dV.$$

(The quantity $\bar{\nu}_{12}$ may be used, if appropriate.) By transforming to spherical polar coordinates,

$$dV = r^2\sin\theta\,d\theta\,d\phi\,dr,$$

the distribution of molecules passing through A, having collided at (r, θ, ϕ), is found to be

$$d\bar{\nu} = \frac{\bar{\nu}_{11}e^{-r/\lambda}}{2\pi}\sin\theta\cos\theta\,dr\,d\theta\,d\phi, \tag{5–25}$$

which is referred to as the *transport distribution*.

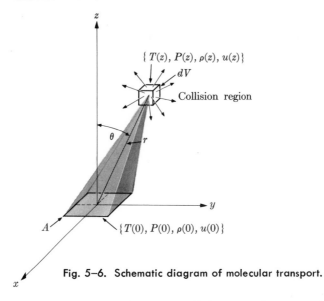

Fig. 5–6. Schematic diagram of molecular transport.

When this expression for a uniform gas is integrated over all space *above the plane*, we obtain for the unilateral transport rate per unit area

$$\bar{\nu}_- = \frac{\lambda \bar{\nu}_{11}}{2}. \tag{5–26}$$

The net transport rate is, of course, zero, since transport of molecules from above the plane is compensated by transport of molecules from below the plane, i.e., $\bar{\nu}_-$ and $\bar{\nu}_+$ are equal in magnitude but are of opposite sign. With the aid of Eqs. (5–17a) and (5–18), we obtain

$$\bar{\nu}_- = \left(\frac{n}{V}\right)\left(\frac{kT}{2\pi m}\right)^{1/2} = \frac{1}{4}\left(\frac{n}{V}\right)\bar{S}.$$

From Eqs. (3–63) and (4–34) the identical result is obtained. This consistency is encouraging. However, we must stress that the values of bimolecular collision frequency and mean free path employed here refer only to *scattering*. They may be replaced, as mentioned earlier, by relevant values for equilibration of various sorts. In that case, Eqs. (5–25) and (5–26) are of general utility, although the various $\bar{\nu}$'s will not conform to the scattering value.

The transport distribution given by Eq. (5–25) is *formally correct*. The relevance of the Maxwell velocity distribution to the nonuniform gas, as mentioned previously, thus seems obscure. However, an evaluation of both $\bar{\nu}_{11}$ (or $\bar{\nu}_{12}$) and λ implicitly involves an averaging over a velocity distribution. The values given by Eqs. (5–17) and (5–18) have invoked the Maxwell distribution. For non-uniform gases, as stated earlier, a somewhat different distribution must be employed. Then, the bimolecular collision frequencies and mean free path will depart somewhat from the expressions we have exhibited, especially in regard to their dependence upon temperature.

The transport phenomena with which we are concerned have two common features: (1) there is no *net* transport of matter through the gas; (2) there exists only a *constant gradient* of temperature, flow velocity, or composition, as the case may be. The first condition is equivalent to the mathematical statement

$$\int_{\text{all space}} d\bar{\nu}(x, y, z) = 0,$$

which we have demonstrated is satisfied for a uniform gas. For a non-uniform gas, both $\bar{\nu}_{11}$ and λ are dependent upon position, and an exact evaluation of the integral is difficult to carry out. When this is done, however, consistency demands that these two quantities be related to each other and the gradients which are involved. As a result, there can be no net transport of any constant (i.e., spatially uniform) property of the molecules. To see this, we define the transport rate of some mean molecular property $\bar{\alpha}(x, y, z)$, where the latter is locally determined at (x, y, z), as

$$-\dot{\alpha} \equiv \int_{\text{all space}} d\bar{\nu}(x, y, z)\bar{\alpha}(x, y, z).$$

From the previous relation, $\dot{\alpha}$ vanishes when $\bar{\alpha}(x, y, z)$ is constant, as for a uniform gas.

The choice of sign in the previous equation has been made to conform to a net transport from above the plane in Fig. 5–6. Since the unilateral transport rate has direction, it must be reckoned as negative with reference to the z-axis. The subscript minus sign indicated in Eq. (5–26) relates to the direction of transport.

When $\bar{\alpha}(x, y, z)$ varies, as in a nonuniform gas, a net transport may occur. In particular, the properties of interest may be limited to vary linearly with z, as shown in Fig. 5–6. Thus, if energy transport is involved, the mean energy of a molecule is

$$\bar{\epsilon}(x, y, z) = \bar{\epsilon}_0 + z c_v \left(\frac{\partial T}{\partial z}\right)_{x,y}, \tag{5–27}$$

making use of Eq. (5–13). Here c_v is the heat capacity per molecule. In the transport of flow momentum, the flow velocity in the gas, parallel to the transport plane, is

$$u(x, y, z) = u_0 + z \left(\frac{\partial u}{\partial z}\right)_{x,y}. \tag{5–28}$$

In the case of binary diffusion, the particle density of the Kth constituent varies as

$$\left(\frac{n_K}{V}\right)(x, y, z) = \left(\frac{n_K}{V}\right)_0 + z\left(\frac{\partial(n_K/V)}{\partial z}\right)_{x,y}. \tag{5–29}$$

A similar variation is obtained for the mole fraction of each constituent. The zero subscript refers to the value in the transport plane. As a result, the transport properties considered here all involve the single integral

$$\int_{\text{all space}} d\bar{\nu}(x, y, z)z = \frac{1}{2\pi}\int_0^{2\pi} d\phi \int_0^{\pi} d\theta \sin\theta \cos^2\theta \int_0^{\infty} dr\, r\bar{\nu}_{11}e^{-r/\lambda},$$

since $z = r\cos\theta$. An approximate value of the integral, satisfactory for our purposes, is obtained by assigning to $\bar{\nu}_{11}$ and λ the values at $z = 0$. Then

$$\int_{\text{all space}} d\bar{\nu}(x, y, z)z = \tfrac{2}{3}\bar{\nu}_{11}\lambda^2. \tag{5–30}$$

The previous equation may be employed for all our transport properties, with the realization that the bimolecular collision frequency and mean free paths pertain to the respective processes. For thermal conductivity, we have (introducing a collision frequency and a mean free path which are appropriate for the process)

$$-\dot{\epsilon} = \tfrac{2}{3}c_v(\bar{\nu}_{11}\lambda^2)_{\text{th}}\left(\frac{\partial T}{\partial z}\right)_{x,y}. \tag{5–31}$$

If we identify the left side with the flow of heat energy, per unit area and per unit time, and identify the terms in Eq. (2–9), we obtain for the coefficient of thermal conductivity

$$\kappa = \tfrac{2}{3}c_v(\bar{\nu}_{11}\lambda^2)_{\text{th}}. \tag{5–32}$$

By an obvious rearrangement, we can obtain (in terms of corresponding quantities for scattering)

$$\kappa = \tfrac{2}{3}c_v(\bar{\nu}_{11}\lambda^2)_{\text{sc}}\left\{\frac{(\bar{\nu}_{11}\lambda^2)_{\text{th}}}{(\bar{\nu}_{11}\lambda^2)_{\text{sc}}}\right\}. \tag{5–33}$$

In more elementary derivations, the term in braces is set equal to unity. More elaborate calculations than we can undertake, involving the dynamics of the collisions, reveal that the ratio is greater than unity. We shall return to this point presently.

In the case of viscous flow, the transport of molecules involves a transport of flow momentum $m\dot{u}$. Analogously to Eq. (5–31), we obtain

$$-(m\dot{u}) = \tfrac{2}{3}m(\bar{\nu}_{11}\lambda^2)_{\text{vis}}\left(\frac{\partial u}{\partial z}\right)_{x,y}. \tag{5–34}$$

Relating the rate of transport of momentum per unit area with a viscous force by Newton's Law of Motion, we can compare with Eq. (2–12) and obtain for the coefficient of viscosity

$$\eta = \tfrac{2}{3}m(\bar{\nu}_{11}\lambda^2)_{\text{sc}}\left\{\frac{(\bar{\nu}_{11}\lambda^2)_{\text{vis}}}{(\bar{\nu}_{11}\lambda^2)_{\text{sc}}}\right\}. \tag{5–35}$$

Here again, the quantity in braces is set equal to unity in more elementary derivations. More elaborate calculations reveal that it is greater than unity.

Assuming that in both Eq. (5–33) and Eq. (5–35) the quantity in braces is a constant, and noticing that

$$(\bar{\nu}_{11}\lambda^2)_{\text{sc}} = \frac{1}{2}\left(\frac{n}{V}\right)\bar{S}\lambda_{\text{sc}} = \frac{1}{\sigma_{12}}\left(\frac{kT}{\pi m}\right)^{1/2}$$

by Eqs. (5–17a), (5–18), and (5–26), we conclude that both κ and η should be independent of the particle density of a gas. This surprising result was obtained first by Maxwell approximately one hundred years ago. It clearly must fail, however, when λ exceeds the size of the gas container. Stressing the intimate relationship between thermal conductivity and viscosity, we have the following:

$$\frac{m\kappa}{\eta} = c_v\left\{\frac{(\bar{\nu}_{11}\lambda^2)_{\text{th}}}{(\bar{\nu}_{11}\lambda^2)_{\text{vis}}}\right\}.$$

This is the relation which suggested the plot in Fig. 2–10. The different slopes there relate to the different heat capacities at constant volume for monatomic and diatomic gases. However, the ratio of the slopes is not 5/3, as expected from the heat capacities. We can interpret this as a variation in the quantity $(\bar{\nu}_{11}\lambda^2)_{\text{th}}/(\bar{\nu}_{11}\lambda^2)_{\text{vis}}$ for the two kinds of molecules.

A more detailed analysis of the transport of energy and momentum has been carried out by various methods. In terms of our results, agreement with more precise results is obtained if we set

$$\left\{\frac{(\bar{\nu}_{11}\lambda^2)_{\text{vis}}}{(\bar{\nu}_{11}\lambda^2)_{\text{sc}}}\right\} = 1.50, \tag{5–36}$$

and

$$\left\{\frac{(\bar{\nu}_{11}\lambda^2)_{\text{th}}}{(\bar{\nu}_{11}\lambda^2)_{\text{sc}}}\right\} = 3.75. \tag{5–37}$$

Even these modifications are approximate, although they give

$$W\kappa = \tfrac{5}{2}\eta C_V, \tag{5-38}$$

which for monatomic gases is in reasonably good agreement with experiment. For polyatomic gases, the numerical coefficient decreases from the value of 2.5 to about 1.4, in the case of ammonia. This behavior suggests that differences may be occurring in the equilibration rates of translational and rotational energies.

The binary diffusion of substances can be treated by the previous mode of analysis. However, care must be given to the fact that now different molecules are involved. In the first place, the rate of binary collisions in any region is dependent upon composition. Specifically, we shall have to deal with a quantity

$$\bar{\nu}^* = \bar{\nu}_{11} + \bar{\nu}_{12} + \bar{\nu}_{22},$$

each term of which relates to collisions among identical or different molecules. The appropriate expressions are given by Eqs. (5–17a) and (5–17b). Secondly, we must alter the analysis if the mean free paths of the two constituents are different. Because the intensity of the mixture leaving each region is the sum of the intensities of the two constituents, Eq. (5–20) cannot be satisfied by mixtures in general. To avoid complexities of this sort, which tend to obscure the essential physical features of the diffusion process, we shall restrict our attention to *self-diffusion*. In such cases, the masses and cross sections are identical for both particles and $\bar{\nu}^*$ can be shown to be equal to $\bar{\nu}_{11}$, while the mean free path of the mixture is identical with those of the constituents. (As noted in Chapter 2, a direct measurement of self-diffusion is impossible. Nevertheless, as the properties of different diffusing species become essentially the same the resulting diffusion process corresponds conceptually to self-diffusion.)

The process of self-diffusion can be viewed as involving the transport of the mole fraction of molecules of interest. Hence the integral of its mole fraction over the transport distribution must be evaluated. As previously, we can obtain for the Kth substance

$$-\dot{n}_K = \tfrac{2}{3}(\bar{\nu}_{11}\lambda^2)_{\mathrm{dif}} \left(\frac{\partial x_K}{\partial z}\right)_{x,y},$$

where x_K is the mole fraction of the Kth substance. Since no net mass transport occurs, we must have (for two substances)

$$(n_1/V)\,(x, y, z) + (n_2/V)\,(x, y, z) = (n/V),$$

the latter being independent of location. Hence

$$-\dot{n}_K = \frac{2}{3} \frac{(\bar{\nu}_{11}\lambda^2)_{\mathrm{dif}}}{(n/V)} \left(\frac{\partial(n_K/V)}{\partial z}\right)_{x,y}. \tag{5-39}$$

Comparison with Fick's Law, Eq. (2–10), yields the diffusion coefficient:

$$D_K = \frac{2}{3} \frac{(\bar{\nu}_{11}\lambda^2)_{sc}}{(n/V)} \left\{ \frac{(\bar{\nu}_{11}\lambda^2)_{dif}}{(\bar{\nu}_{11}\lambda^2)_{sc}} \right\}. \tag{5–40}$$

By construction, we see that an identical equation is obtained for the diffusion coefficient of the other substance, independent of composition. Contrasted with the behavior of the coefficients of thermal conductivity and viscosity, the diffusion coefficient varies inversely as the particle density, in good accord with experiment.

A more detailed analysis of diffusion has been carried out. To bring Eq. (5–40) into agreement with the more precise result requires that

$$\left\{ \frac{(\bar{\nu}_{11}\lambda^2)_{dif}}{(\bar{\nu}_{11}\lambda^2)_{sc}} \right\} = 1.78. \tag{5–41}$$

This value is, however, approximate. A comparison of the coefficients of diffusion and viscosity gives, upon some manipulation,

$$WD = 1.18\eta\bar{V}, \tag{5–42}$$

$\bar{V}$ being the molal volume of the gas. This relation motivated the correlation shown in Fig. 2–11. Experimentally, larger values of the coefficient are obtained, such as 1.37 for hydrogen.

Equations (5–36), (5–37), and (5–41) comprise an interesting triad, for the following reason. From the form of the bimolecular collision frequency, Eq. (5–17a), and that for the mean free path, Eq. (5–18), we see that $(\bar{\nu}_{11}\lambda)$ is independent of the cross section. Hence $(\bar{\nu}_{11}\lambda^2)$ is inversely proportional to the cross section of the process involved. We may, therefore, make the interpretation that the cross sections for all three transport processes *are smaller* than those for *scattering* (i.e., deflection). Furthermore, the cross sections for diffusion and viscosity are similar, while that for energy transfer is smallest. These relations are only qualitative, but seem reasonably in accord with our anticipations.

Nevertheless, in spite of its reasonableness, this interpretation must be used with caution. The more detailed theory which leads to Eqs. (5–36), (5–37), and (5–41), due to Chapman and Enskog, makes no explicit distinction in the cross sections for the various transport processes. In this theory, as indicated earlier, the *nonuniform* velocity distribution accompanying each transport process must be employed to evaluate average collision frequencies which are pertinent. These differ from the expressions given in Eqs. (5–16), (5–17a), and (5–17b) because of the different velocity distributions which are employed for each process. However, the *form* which has been given is maintained in the more precise theory; only the factor multiplying the geometrical cross section differs. Hence, while we may conclude that $(\bar{\nu}_{11}\lambda^2)$ is inversely proportional to the geometrical cross section, the variations which do occur in $(\bar{\nu}_{11}\lambda^2)$ relate to the constants of proportionality in each transport process. If we insist upon the form of the simple theory treated here, we must ascribe different values of the proportionality constants to *effective geometrical cross sections* which then differ from one transport property to another. Such an insistence is entirely arbitrary, to be sure, but conveniently reconciles the simple theory with more precise results.

5. THE COVOLUME EQUATION OF STATE

In order to simplify the previous analysis, so as to keep the physical essentials clear, we have tacitly assumed that the density of particles (n/V) is small. As a result, the effect of molecular size upon bimolecular collision frequencies and mean free paths has been found to depend only upon the effective cross sections of the molecules. However, at the very outset there is a difficulty. Recalling the derivations leading to Eqs. (5–16), (5–17a), and (5–17b) for the collision frequencies, we have used the particle density (n/V) to estimate the number of molecules to be found in a volume swept out by a specified molecule. These molecules represent the possible scatterers. Analogously, Eq. (5–24) has involved the same reasoning for the mean free path. But suppose that the particle density is great enough so that a specified molecule cannot pass between the others. How can it then sweep out the volume associated with these calculations? The obvious answer is that it cannot do so, and our present task is to rectify the theory to take this behavior into account.

It must be stated at the outset that the condition we have just mentioned corresponds to a restriction to be imposed upon the attainable particle densities of gases. From the properties of gases at high pressures, as exhibited in the covolume equation of state of the form of Eq. (1–26), this behavior is in accord with experiment. We may, therefore, proceed with confidence in the physical correctness of the above idea.

There is another factor to be kept in mind. Under the influence of attractive intermolecular potentials, there will be a tendency toward *molecular clustering*. This tendency can be discerned from Eq. (5–1), which will reveal larger values for ρ_2 when ϕ is negative. One effect of clustering will be to restrict the transport of particles from each region of the gas to other regions. This can be expected to give rise to negative deviations from ideality. Another effect of clustering will be to provide an increase in the molecular weight of the gas. (Recall the extreme case of a diatomic gas, considered in Section 1.) This also will contribute to negative deviations from ideality.

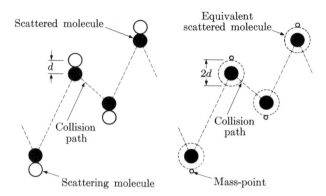

Fig. 5–7. Correspondence between hard-sphere collisions and mass-points.

If the molecules are represented as impenetrable spheres of diameter d, the distance of closest approach between the centers of molecules also is d. In terms of relative motion, the behavior of the scattered molecule may be regarded as equivalent to that of a sphere of diameter $2d$, while the remaining gas molecules are regarded as mass-points. This is indicated in Fig. 5–7. In these terms, our calculations have estimated the number of mass-points of particle density (n/V) which may be found in the volume swept out by the scattered molecule. (However, the diagram indicates that the mass-points never actually fall within the boundaries because of changing directions of the scattered molecule.) Most important for our present considerations is the fact that the fictitious mass-points have also a minimum distance of approach. This value also is d. As a result, each molecular center of mass is associated with a volume of $(4\pi/3)\,d^3$ which *excludes* all other molecules of the gas. Since this is shared *pairwise* between molecules of the gas, each molecule of the gas contributes, on the average, a volume of $(2\pi/3)\,d^3$ which is inaccessible to the centers of mass of the others. Since the volume of such a molecule is $(4\pi/3)\,(d/2)^3$, the unavailable volume per molecule is four times its own volume.

Now, if there are n molecules in a volume V, the previous considerations lead us to conclude that the average volume *accessible to a colliding molecule* is $(V - nb)$, where b is four molecular volumes. It is this *free volume* which must be used in our calculation, for only in this region can the scattered molecule be found, on the average. For a uniform particle density, the number of scattering molecules encountered by the scattered molecule in a unit of time is proportional to the ratio of swept-out volume to free volume, that is,

$$\frac{\pi\,d^2|\mathbf{v}^{\mathrm{rel}}|}{V - nb}.$$

The average number of collisions per unit time is the product of this ratio and the total number n. Consequently, we obtain

$$\bar{\nu}_1 = \left(\frac{n}{V - nb}\right) 4\pi d^2 \left(\frac{kT}{\pi m}\right)^{1/2}, \qquad (5\text{–}43)$$

instead of Eq. (5–16). Since the colliding molecules are confined to the free volume of the gas, the effective density of such molecules is greater than the ordinary density. Making use of the definition of the mean free path, we obtain

$$\lambda = \frac{1}{\sqrt{2}\pi d^2[n/(V - nb)]} \qquad (5\text{–}44)$$

instead of Eq. (5–18).

To correct our previous expression for the binary collision frequency, we consider a small volume dV. The number of *colliding* molecules which can be found in this volume is simply the product of the total number and the fraction of free volume covered by dV. The result is $n\, dV/(V - nb)$. Since each of these molecules has an average collision frequency given by $\bar{\nu}_1$, above, the average bimolecular collision frequency, per unit of volume, is

$$\bar{\nu}_{11} = \left(\frac{n}{V - nb}\right)^2 \cdot 2\pi d^2 \left(\frac{kT}{\pi m}\right)^{1/2}, \qquad (5\text{–}45)$$

instead of Eq. (5–17a). The modification for $\bar{\nu}_{12}$ is easily made along the above lines, but we shall not do so. Note that Eqs. (5–43) through (5–45) reduce, as they must, to the previous ones for $(n/V) \to 0$.

The representation of molecules as hard spheres certainly is incorrect. The approximation involved neglects the attractive forces prevailing between molecules, as indicated in Fig. 5–1. Nevertheless, the effect of the repulsive region is properly accounted for: molecules in the gas can coexist with intermolecular distances corresponding to the attractive region, but essentially not with intermolecular distances corresponding to the repulsive region. Thus Eqs. (5–43) through (5–45) may still be employed, with the modification that πd^2 is replaced by an appropriate cross section for the scattering process. However, the effect of attractive forces between molecules involves something more.

A molecule which leaves any region in which it has had its last collision may be assumed to have an intermolecular distance between it and all others that is greater than the range of attractive forces. In the present case a steady state exists, so that the molecules which may leave a region must come from that fraction having negligible interaction with the others. The estimation of this fraction is difficult to carry out precisely in a simple manner. Nevertheless, we can guess that it must be less than unity. Furthermore, we can anticipate that it must decrease as the particle density increases, since the region of negligible interaction necessarily decreases with increasing particle density. As the particle density goes to zero, this fraction must approach unity, for corresponding reasons. The effect of the attractive forces may be seen to modify only the transport distribution.

We now turn to the problem of approximating the equation of state of a gas of molecules having size. To do so, we recall our earlier treatment of the ideal gas, in Chapter 3. We need to compute the rate of momentum transfer per unit area produced by collisions with a plate. Figure 5–6 may be used for this purpose. From the volume element dV, we imagine a narrow beam of molecules approaching the origin. These have an average speed $\bar{s}$ [in units of $(kT/m)^{1/2}$] associated with the distribution we have obtained for a narrow molecular beam, Eq. (4–39). Hence,

$$\bar{s} = \tfrac{1}{2}\int_0^\infty ds\ s^4 e^{-s^2/2}.$$

After evaluating the integral, we find that

$$\bar{s} = \tfrac{3}{4}(2\pi)^{1/2}.$$

If the molecules are reflected at the origin, there will be an impulse transmitted perpendicular to the plate. The momentum change associated with this impulse is twice the magnitude of the z-component of momentum. In ordinary units, this quantity is $2m \cos \theta \cdot \tfrac{3}{4}(2\pi kT/m)^{1/2}$, and this must be integrated over the transport distribution for all regions above the plane. We may immediately relate the resulting quantity (since it implicitly refers to a unit area) to the pressure. One then obtains, with the aid of Eq. (5–25),

$$P = \tfrac{3}{2}(2\pi mkT)^{1/2}\int_{\substack{\text{upper}\\\text{volume}}} d\bar{\nu}\ \cos \theta$$

$$= \frac{3}{4\pi}(2\pi mkT)^{1/2}\int_0^{2\pi} d\phi \int_0^{\pi/2} d\theta \int_0^\infty dr \sin \theta \cos^2 \theta\ \bar{\nu}_{11}e^{-r/\lambda},$$

where $\bar{\nu}_{11}$ and λ are here given by Eqs. (5–44) and (5–45). Since the gas is uniform, these quantities do not depend upon position. Hence we obtain

$$P = \tfrac{1}{2}(2\pi mkT)^{1/2}\bar{\nu}_{11}\lambda = \left(\frac{n}{V-nb}\right)kT, \qquad (5\text{–}46)$$

with the aid of Eqs. (5–44) and (5–45). This expression can be recognized as the *covolume equation of state*, which was discussed in Chapter 1, expressed in terms of the molecular volume.

In view of the previous discussion of the effect of attractive forces, Eq. (5–46) must be modified by the inclusion of a density-dependent factor less than unity, corresponding to a correction for the internal pressure of a gas. Although qualitatively correct, we shall not present it. For anything with a more secure theoretical basis it is advisable to proceed differently. This also we shall not do. We only note that the general Maxwell-Boltzmann distribution, an extension of Eqs. (4–49) and (5–1), provides the theoretical apparatus for obtaining the equilibrium values of *all* molecular properties, without the necessity of emphasizing the kinetic behavior of the molecules. This sort of approach is adopted by *equilibrium statistical mechanics* and is the only really satisfactory theoretical way of obtaining precise results for the equilibrium properties of real gases.

6. SUMMARY

The modifications of ideal gas theory which must be made have been related to the repulsive and attractive interactions between molecules.

The behavior of diatomic molecules has been considered as the first example of nonideal behavior, due to the strong interactions between atoms. The rotational motion has been examined for the rigid diatomic molecule. The heat capacities of such molecules is in good accord with the calculated results and suggests that vibrational motion may be "quenched."

The transport properties of thermal conductivity, viscosity, and diffusion have been considered. Expressions for the relevant coefficients have been obtained in terms of molecular properties. The analysis requires the construction of a transport distribution which relates to the number of molecules which have collided in a small region and leave it. Correlations previously exhibited between the transport properties have been justified theoretically.

The effect of molecular size on the equation of state has been examined. It was found to relate to the positive deviations from ideality and led to the covolume equation of state. Negative deviations from ideality were mentioned, but not exhibited.

EXERCISES

1. Determine the heat capacity per particle for a monatomic gas confined to an indefinitely long tube whose axis coincides with a uniform gravitational field. *Answer:* $\frac{5}{2}k$.

2. A reasonable but approximate treatment of the vibration of a diatomic molecule takes the interatomic potential to be

$$\phi(r^{(\text{rel})}) = C(r^{(\text{rel})} - r_0)^2,$$

with $C/kT \gg 1$. Combine this with Eq. (5–9) to obtain a *vibrational distribution density*, and evaluate the mean energy of vibration (kinetic plus potential). (Disregard the limitation discussed in the text dealing with unbound atoms.)

Answer: kT.

3. Consider a forest which has trees with an average diameter of one foot. Although the trees are randomly spaced, their number density averages to about 1000/acre. (1 acre $\approx$ 43,560 ft².) A boy (one foot in diameter) who is blindfolded starts at an arbitrary tree and walks in a randomly oriented straight line. (a) How far will he have to walk on the average to bump into another tree? (b) What is the average distance between trees?

Answers: (a) About 22 ft; (b) about 12 ft.

4. Show that β of Eq. (5–24) is not less than unity. (Note that some simplification occurs if the origin of velocity is taken as the beam velocity.)

5. The probability that a molecule will have a free path l is expressed (with appropriate changes of notation) by Eq. (5–22). Assume a specific velocity v_0 of the molecule and obtain the following expression for the lifetime (between collisions) probability of a molecule:

$$dM = \frac{1}{\tau} e^{-(t-t_0)/\tau} dt,$$

where $\tau = \lambda/v_0$ is the mean time between collisions.

6. (a) Evaluate the dispersion in free paths experienced by a molecule.
   (b) Do the same for lifetimes.
   (c) Determine the median lifetime.

Answers: (a) λ^2; (b) τ^2; (c) 0.694τ.

7. From the values of Table 2–1, determine the effective molecular diameter of an oxygen molecule.

Answer: $3.64 \cdot 10^{-8}$ cm (viscosity).

8. Using the relation that the covolume is four times the molecular volume, estimate van der Waals' a and b for oxygen, using the results of Exercise 7 and the critical pressure in Table 1–4. Compare with Table 1–5.

Answers: $4.90\,1^2 \cdot$ atm/(gm-mole)²; 0.0604 liter/gm-mole.

9. The expressions we have obtained for the transport rate of a mean molecular property correspond intuitively to the product of the unilateral transport rate and the difference in the values of the mean molecular property at some mean distance above and below the transport plane. To illustrate,

$$-\dot{\epsilon} = \bar{\nu}_-\{\bar{\epsilon}(0, 0, \bar{z}_+) - \bar{\epsilon}(0, 0, \bar{z}_-)\},$$

where $\bar{z}_+$ is the average distance of the last collision of the molecules passing the transport plane from above. Show that this expression and those for viscosity and difference lead to the transport equations. Evaluate $\bar{z}_+$.

Answer: $\frac{2}{3} \cdot \lambda$.

10. Calculate the self-diffusion coefficient for oxygen at STP, using the results of Exercise 7.

Answer: 0.159 cm²/sec.

REFERENCES

CHAPMAN, S., and T. G. COWLING, *The Mathematical Theory of Non-uniform Gases*, Cambridge University Press, Cambridge, 1958.

FRENKEL, J., *Kinetic Theory of Liquids*, Dover Publications, Inc., New York, 1955.

HIRSCHFELDER, J. O., C. F. CURTISS, and R. B. BIRD, *Molecular Theory of Gases and Liquids*, John Wiley and Sons, Inc., New York, 1954.

JEANS, J. H., *The Dynamical Theory of Gases*, Fourth Edition, Dover Publications, Inc., New York, 1954.

KENNARD, E. H., *Kinetic Theory of Gases*, McGraw-Hill Book Co., Inc., New York, 1938.

NASH, L. K., *The Atomic-Molecular Theory*, Harvard University Press, Cambridge, 1956.

PARTINGTON, J. R., *An Advanced Treatise on Physical Chemistry*, Vol. I, Longmans, Green and Co., London, 1949.

SEARS, F. W., *Thermodynamics, The Kinetic Theory of Gases, and Statistical Mechanics*, Addison-Wesley Publishing Co., Inc., Reading, 1959.

INDEX

Angular momentum, 70
Average, 79, 81, 92
  molecular, 81, 92
Avogadro, constant, 82, 115
  hypothesis, 14

Barometric formula, 115
Binary collision frequency, 132
Boltzmann, constant, 82
  distribution, 114
    test of, 115
  equation, 137
Boyle's Law, 13
Bunsen calorimeter, 42
Buoyancy, 5

Center of mass, 67
Central field, 70
Central force, 66
Charles's Law, 14
Chemical composition, 9
Collisions, 71
  coplanar, 71
  elastic, 77
  frequency of, 132
  "head-on," 73
  lifetime between, 132, 150
  rate of, 85
Compressibility, of condensing system,
    22
  isothermal coefficient, 16
Conceptual experiment, 17
Conductivity, thermal, 43
Conservative force, 65
Constant of motion, 68
Conversion factor, 7
Coordinates, polar, 107
  spherical polar, 108
Corresponding States Relation, 36
Covolume, 25, 146
  deviations due to, 26
Critical constants, Berthelot gas, 38
  Dieterici gas, 35
  table of, 23
  van der Waals gas, 35

Critical phenomena, 23, 34
Critical point, conditions for, 34
Critical pressure, 23
Critical temperature, 22
Critical volume, 23
Cross section, 133

Dalton, 61
  Law of Partial Pressures, 19, 83
Degree of freedom, 130
Density, 12
  probability, 99
Deviations, from ideality, 21, 24
  negative, 21, 27
  positive, 21, 27
Diatomic molecule, 122
Diffusion, 49
  self, 57, 143
Diffusion coefficient(s), 51, 52, 144
  table of, gases, 52
    liquids, 53
Diffusivity, 51
Dimensionality, of equations, 10,
    13
Dispersion, 94
Distribution, 93, 94
  continuous, 100
  discrete, 101
  energy, 110
  frequency, 99
  function, 100
  internal, 125
  joint, 95
  Maxwell-Boltzmann, 114, 121
  multiple molecular, 116
  rotational, 127
  singular, 94
  speed, 109, 121
    in beam, 111
    test of, 112
  symmetric, 97
  transport, 138
  two-dimensional velocity, 107
  velocity, 101
Dynamical properties, 40

Effusion rate, 86
  relative, table of, 87
Energy, diatomic molecule, 128
  internal, 83
  transfer, 74, 90
Equation of state, Berthelot's, 30
  caloric, 83
  covolume, 25, 148
  Dieterici, 31
  of ideal gas, 15, 16
  virial, 31
Equilibration, 137
Equilibrium, distance, 128
  nonuniform, 41
Equipartition theorem, 130
Experiment, conceptual, 17
Extensive variables, 11

Fick's First Law, 51
Fick's Second Law, 51
Flow, laminar, 55
Fluid, 24
  manometric, 6
Force, couple, 54
Fourier, Law of heat conduction, 46
Free volume, 25, 146
Fusion, latent heat of, 42

Gas burette, 4
Gases, nonuniform, 40
Graham, Law of Effusion, 86, 87

Heat, 42
  capacity, 83
    gases, tables of, 83, 129
  flow, 42
  mechanical equivalent of, 42, 83
Heterogeneous mixture, 21
Histogram, 98

Ideal gas, constant, 15, 82, 83
  equation of state, 82
  pressure, 19, 79
  properties, 61
Ideality, deviations from, 21, 24
Impulse, 64, 77
Intensive variables, 11
Isotherm, 21
Isotropy, 82, 102

Jacobian, 118, 127

Kinetic energy, 64
Knudsen, 87, 88

Liouville's Theorem, 114
Liquefaction, 21
Liquid state, 24
Loschmidt number, 88

Mass transport, 49
Maxwell, argument regarding van
      der Waals' gas, 29
  velocity distribution, 101, 104
Mean free path, 132, 134
Measurement, of force, 5
  of mass, 5
  of pressure, 5, 6
  of temperature, 8
  of volume, 4
Mechanics, classical, 62
Median, 107
Mixing, diffusive, 43
Mixture, of ideal gases, 17
Mole fraction, definition, 10
Molecular beam, 110, 133
Molecular clustering, 145
Molecular weight, 9
  correction to, 32
  mean, 20
  relative, 60
  transport properties, 57
Moment, 93
  of inertia, 128
Momentum, 64
Mortality fraction, 134

Newton, Laws of Motion, 62
Nonuniform velocity distribution, 144
Normal boiling constants, table of, 29
Normal error curve, 105

Perrin, 115
Persistence of velocities, 137
Phase, 21
Poise, 55
Pressure, critical, 23
  of a gas, 5
  hydrostatic, 6
  internal, 26, 39
  negative, 28
  partial, 19
  reduced, 36

table of conversion factors, 8
vapor, 19
Properties, extensive, 2
intensive, 2

Quenching, of motion, 130

Reduced equation of state, Dieterici, 36
van der Waals, 36
Reduced mass, 67

Self-diffusion, 57, 143
Shear stress, 54
Specific volumes, table of, 12
Speed, average, 106
mean, 84
relative, average, 117, 119
root-mean-square, 84
State, of gas, 3
location, 3
macroscopic, 40
of nonuniform gas, 41
stationary, 42
variable, 4
reduced, 36
States, Corresponding, 35
metastable, of van der Waals'
gas, 29
Static properties, 40
Statistical independence, 96
Stokes' equation, 89, 90
STP, 15

Temperature, Boyle, 32
celsius scale, 8
critical, 22
fahrenheit scale, 8
kelvin scale, 15
reduced, 36
Thermal conductivity, coefficient of,
46, 141
table of coefficients, gases, 47
liquids and solids, 49

Thermal expansion, coefficient, 17
Thermodynamics, 29, 42
Thermostat, 9
Time-average, 79
Transport properties, 43
correlation among, 57
Transport rate, 139, 140

Units, of chemical composition, 10
of force, 6
of pressure, 8

Van der Waals, constants, mixtures,
33
table of, 29
equation of state, 28
gas, 28
Vapor, 19
pressure, 19, 21
state, 24
Variables, continuous, 100
Vector equation, 47, 69
Velocity, selection, 110
Virial coefficients, 31
Viscosity coefficient, 55, 142
table, of gases, 47
liquids, 56
Viscosity equation, Newton's, 55
Viscous behavior, of fluid, 54
Viscous force, 54
Volume, critical, 23
displaced, 5
molal, of ideal gas, 15
reduced, 36
specific, 11
table of, 12
units, 4

Walls, collision with, 76
Weight, 5
Weight fraction, definition, 10
Work, 65